SOLO DUO·TRIO

Puzzles and Games
for Building
English Language Skills

Richard Yorkey

Illustrations by Andrew Toos

PRO LINGUA **ASSOCIATES**

Pro Lingua Associates, Publishers
15 Elm Street
Brattleboro, Vermont 05301 USA
Office 802 257 7779
Orders 800 366 4775
Email prolingu@siver.net
SAN 216-0579

At Pro Lingua,
our objective is to foster an approach
to learning and teaching that we call
***interplay**, the **inter**action of language*
learners and teachers with their materials,
with the language and culture,
and with each other in active, creative,
*and productive **play**.*

Most of the illustrations in this book are by Andrew Toos. This book was designed and set by Arthur A. Burrows using Century Schoolbook and a variety of other text and display types. The book was printed and bound by D. B. Hess Company in Woodstock, Illinois.

Printed in the United States of America.

First printing 1997. 3000 copies in print.

Contents

The Puzzles and Games

To the Teacher

These puzzles were originally prepared while I was teaching a class of students of varying levels of proficiency and language backgrounds. To give fair attention to each group of students, I needed supplementary materials to facilitate meeting their special needs. During certain classes, I arranged for a few students to read silently, others to write in their daily journals, and some to work on paper-and-pencil puzzles like these to keep them interested and busy, while I worked with another group of students.

The puzzles were also useful whenever a little time was left at the end of a class period, or a class was shortened because of a meeting, holiday, or fire drill – those times when a teacher needs activities to fill an unexpected break. I filed the material in manila folders, and I called it *The Whole Kit and Caboodle*. Whenever the occasion demanded, I quickly selected a puzzle and reproduced it for the students.

In published format, the puzzles can be used in much the same way as *The Whole Kit and Caboodle* was. I think of *Solo, Duo, Trio* as material for harried teachers who often need to resort to time-fillers or reproducible exercises that focus clearly on one skill or one topic. The puzzles can be photocopied and distributed to individual students, to pairs or small groups, or to an entire class. However you use them, be available to offer whatever learning assistance is necessary. Remember: your purpose is to help students learn, not simply to give them answers. Use a Socratic method, ask students questions, and try to draw them out in hopes that they themselves can discover the appropriate answers.

In class. Puzzles can be selected either to focus on a particular point to be learned, or simply to provide entertaining but useful language practice. Students might work on the same puzzle simultaneously, or each student may work independently, at his or her own ability and speed. Sharing a puzzle, pairs will often discuss their answers, enhancing both their enjoyment and their learning. As the teacher, you are the best person to decide between individualized and group work on any particular day. In the following sections, there are suggestions on how to make effective use of each kind of puzzle or game.

In a learning center. Many programs centralize individualized materials in a language lab or self-access learning center. Each of the puzzles might be duplicated and multiple copies labeled and filed in a cabinet for students to choose from. One file might include all the Answer Keys so that students can check their own work. You may wish to set up some system to help students keep a record of which puzzles they have successfully completed. However, it's important to emphasize the ***pleasure*** of the puzzles rather than the necessity to complete or be graded on a certain number of them!

In the library. Some programs maintain a library of extensive readers or other books for students to sign out and enjoy. Several copies of *Solo, Duo, Trio* might be included, or a file of masters made available that can be duplicated upon request.

Introduction to Using the Puzzles

The instructions for each type of puzzle are repeated on each puzzle. They are written simply and often depend on examples because students may be working on their own. However, in introducing the puzzles to less proficient students, you may need to be available to answer questions.

As the title *Solo, Duo, Trio* suggests, these activities are designed to be used by students working alone or with one or more friends. Working solo allows students to reflect on what they're doing, take their time, and experiment with being self-reliant, by using a dictionary, for example. On the other hand, duos and trios sharing a puzzle will work cooperatively through tough spots, discuss the meaning of vocabulary or the implication of a proverb, and have fun playing with the language together. The benefits of student- centered cooperative work, of discussion focused on the language and culture, and of enjoying the learning process are very far-reaching. Using puzzles and games like these individually, in pairs, or in small groups helps establish the relaxed, communicative classroom atmosphere that frees students young and old to learn naturally, even when the learning activities are less entertaining.

The explanations and suggestions that follow go beyond the simple instructions given on each puzzle. They don't cover all of the types of puzzles, and they don't group puzzles in the sequence in which they appear in the book. The reason is simply that I have some helpful suggestions to make about the puzzles that involve reading, proverbs, and word searches.

Reading

The kind of reading activities in *Solo, Duo, Trio* are different from most reading comprehension exercises. They focus on the word level *(Anagrams)*, on the search for meaning by intelligent guessing *(Top-Half Reading)*, on sequence signals *(Jumbled Stories)*, and on topic lexicon and connotations *(What Are You Reading?)*.

Jumbled Stories. (PAGE 15)

This activity is a variation of strip stories, adapted for individual students rather than a group. Each student should look for the beginning sentence of the story. Once that has been identified, the student should carefully consider the other sentences, looking for sequence signals *(then, next, finally, later...)*, pronoun references *(...her father. He...)*, and the logical sequence of ideas, actions, dialogue, and plot.

Extended practice for the Jumbled Stories. Once elementary level students have correctly arranged the sentences into a meaningful order, they can copy the story, sentence by sentence. For many students this is not as simple as the teacher might expect! For oral practice, students might prepare to read the story aloud, or memorize it so that they can speak it with correct pronunciation and appropriate intonation and emphasis. Then either you or a student who has read it well aloud, might dictate the story to the class, perhaps with punctuation. At a higher level, students might be encouraged to prepare their own jumbled story. About five or six lines is a good number. Be sure there is only one way in which the story can be reassembled, and that there are adequate language signals to help students.

Top-Half Reading. (PAGE 21)

Many ESL students are afraid to guess! They feel that they must have *all* the information before they can comprehend a passage. This is not necessarily true! In fact, this activity will prove to them that they can read with only 50% of the information. Using what they already know about English spelling, grammar, and vocabulary, they can easily figure out each of these stories, often much to their surprise.

Extended practice for Top-Half Reading. To prove that they have been able to guess the meaning by reading only the upper half of the letters, students can copy each story (as with the Jumbled Stories). They can also get oral practice by reading the story aloud, with suitable expression. You may want to demonstrate how much more difficult it is, if not impossible, to read by using only the bottom half of the line. Hint: You can prepare your own "bottom-half reading" exercises. Use a computer to print a story with rather large type (14 point Times is a good font and size). Use correction tape to cover the top half of the line. Then photocopy the page.

What Are You Reading? (PAGE 31)

In this activity, students focus on clues to help them identify the general topic they are reading about. Format and typography are useful, but content, as determined by vocabulary, contributes to deciding the topic. Just a quick look at a small sample is often enough to make an intelligent guess. When using this activity with a group of students, discuss the kinds of information that helped them recognize each of the topics.

Proverbs

Three of the puzzle types use proverbs. Why? As traditional sayings, proverbs can be a gold mine of material for English teaching. They offer advice or present a moral in a short, pithy statement, and they exist in all languages. Generally a proverb may express a general truth, such as *Seeing is believing* or *Bad news travels fast*. Or a proverb may imply a general conclusion from a specific instance, such as *You can lead a horse to water, but you can't make it drink,* or *Don't put all your eggs in one basket*. Many proverbs go back several centuries, but new proverbs are being created all the time. From computers, we now have *Garbage in, garbage out*. And from economics, *There is no such thing as a free lunch.*

The three types of puzzles in this book that use proverbs are *Matching Proverbs,* *Hidden Wisdom Puzzles,* and *Double-Crostic Puzzles.* After some specific comments on these puzzle types, there are some general suggestions for procedures and for extended practice.

Matching Proverbs. (PAGE 7)

These are well-known proverbs that students are likely to hear or read, but they are broken in half and grouped according to similar structural constituents. Students should be asked to use their knowledge of English vocabulary and grammar, reading comprehension, and common sense to make the connection between the first and second parts of the proverbs. A process of elimination might be useful. Urge the students to first connect those they are sure of, then try to figure out the remaining ones.

Hidden Wisdom Puzzles. (PAGE 79)

This puzzle type is likely to be new to students. They're often more comfortable working in pairs the first time they do this kind of puzzle or any other with an unfamiliar format. With a less confident class, it will help to solve one of the samples working as a class on the board. Then have the students pair up and give the pairs copies of the first puzzle to solve. Encourage the students to use their vocabularies and knowledge of English spelling and grammar. Once they learn the puzzle strategy, they will discover that all the answers are common proverbs.

Double-Crostic Puzzles. (PAGE 107)

In these puzzles, in order to learn new proverbs, student are asked to identify words using their definitions and context clues in sample sentences. The students then write each word, letter by letter, on a series of blanks, each one of which is numbered. When they put all these numbered letters in numerical order into the form below, they will be able to read the proverb or an amusing statement in English. Although it is intriguing to work with, the double-crostic format is admittedly a bit complicated, so less confident students will be helped by working in pairs while you are available to give help, at least initially.

General procedures for the "proverb puzzles."

For individuals. After they have gained enough confidence to do so, students will find working on these puzzles solo particularly enjoyable. Follow-up work can then be done in groups.

Paired practice. A good way for students to practice conversation, particularly using modal auxiliaries in a natural context, is by working in pairs. Sitting side by side, they can talk with each other as they try to solve the puzzle together. For example, here is a typical conversation of a pair of students as they work to solve a double-crostic:

"Well, the word might be *arrest*."

"No, it can't be. __ __ RST has only five letters."

"What about *worst*? The letter before RST has to be a vowel."

"You're right about that. But it could be *I,* as in *first.*"

"Yes, yes! Maybe W__ __K is *week*. Then it says *The first day of the week.*"

"But maybe Sunday is the worst day of the week."

For groups. When students all work on the same puzzle, discuss the answer and encourage students to relate it in some way to their own experience. For advanced students, it might be interesting to challenge them to write their own Double-Crostics or Hidden Wisdom Puzzles.

Extended practice for the "proverb puzzles."

For all the puzzles that involve proverbs, you may want to consider the following suggestions for additional language practice.

1. **"Translate" the proverb.** Ask students to express the idea of the proverb in their own words.

   Example: An apple a day keeps the doctor away = If you eat an apple every day, you will stay healthy.

   Example: Don't put all your eggs in one basket = It is wise not to invest all of your money in one place.
   or: Don't put all your trust in only one person.

2. **Appropriate situations.** Ask students to briefly describe a situation in which the proverb might be used.

   Example: If wishes were horses, beggars would ride. One time my best friend saw a very expensive sports car. She told me, "I wish I had a car like that!" "Yes," I replied, "and if wishes were horses, beggars would ride."

   Example: The early bird catches the worm. I wanted to get a good seat at the rock concert, but when I arrived, all the good seats were already taken. A friend who had one of the good seats laughed at me and said, "Well, after all, the early bird catches the worm!"

3. **Similar proverbs in other languages.** Since proverbial statements tend to be universal insights, you're likely to find your students will offer a similar proverb in their native language.

   Example: In English one says, *A bird in the hand is worth two in the bush.*
   In Arabic one says, *A bird in the hand is worth ten on the tree.*

   Take time to discuss these similar proverbs, ways in which they differ, and where and when they might be used.

Crossword Puzzles. (PAGE 59)

A final note on the Crossword Puzzles. In this form, the students are given the word, not a definition. The words are grouped according to the number of letters in the word. To start, if there is one six-letter word, for example, it goes in the one six-letter space. It may be helpful to show this to students who find puzzles difficult.

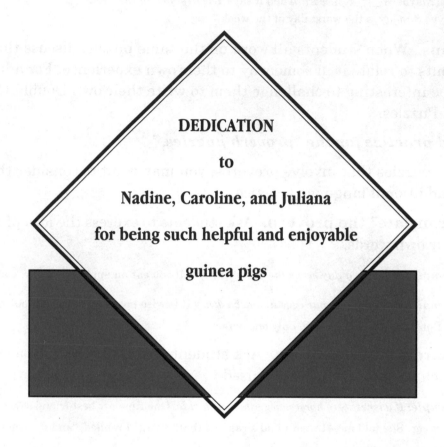

DEDICATION

to

Nadine, Caroline, and Juliana

for being such helpful and enjoyable

guinea pigs

✎ An Anagram Story

Instructions

This is an anagram puzzle: S_____. The answer to the puzzle is STORY.
ROTY
Solve the anagrams in this story, and then read the story aloud.

Last week I went to the T_____. I had a very good S_____ , and
REHEAT   ATE

the P_____ was interesting. But I could not E_____ it because a
AYL   JONY

young man and W_____ were sitting behind me, and they were T_____
MONA   KALNIG

very loudly. Because I could not hear the A_____ on the stage, I became
CORTS

A_____. I turned around and T_____ the people behind me, "I can't
GYRN   LOD

hear a W_____."
ROD

"It's none of your B_____!" the young man said. This is a
SINUSES

P_____ conversation."
TAVIRE

Note: True anagrams are two real words which use the same letters in different order; EAT and ATE are true anagrams.
For these puzzles, I don't use the first letter of the missing word in its anagram because I give that first letter as a clue. And in
these puzzles, some of the words I have used as anagrams are "nonsense words." For example, S_____ + ROTY = STORY.

SOLO, DUO, TRIO: Puzzles and Games. Reproduced with permission. Copyright © 1997 by Richard Yorkey
Published by PRO LINGUA ASSOCIATES, 15 Elm Street, Brattleboro, Vermont 05301 USA 800 366 4775

✏️ An Anagram Story

Abe Lincoln was a new L_____ . One time he
YAWRE

asked a young boy, "If I C_____ a dog's tail a leg, how
LAL

many L_____ would the dog have?"
GES

The boy A_____ brightly. "F_____."
REDNEWS   VIE

Lincoln said, "No, still only F_____ legs. Just calling a
URO

T_____ a leg doesn't M_____ it a leg!"
LIA   EKA

SOLO, DUO, TRIO: Puzzles and Games. Reproduced with permission. Copyright © 1997 by Richard Yorkey
Published by PRO LINGUA ASSOCIATES, 15 Elm Street, Brattleboro, Vermont 05301 USA 800 366 4775

✏️ An Anagram Story

Bishop Jones was sometimes absent-minded. He would

F_____ important N_____ and appointments. Once he
GORTE   MESA

was traveling by T_____ to attend a conference. He had
NIRA

F_____ his T_____ , but the conductor
ETGONROT   CITEK

T_____him. "Don't W_____ , Bishop Jones. We K_____
DOL   RORY   WON

who you are!"

"That's all very well," said B_____ Jones. "But W_____
IPOSH   OTUTHI

a ticket, how am I to know where I'm G_____?"
NIGO

SOLO, DUO, TRIO: Puzzles and Games. Reproduced with permission. Copyright © 1997 by Richard Yorkey
Published by PRO LINGUA ASSOCIATES, 15 Elm Street, Brattleboro, Vermont 05301 USA 800 366 4775

✏️ An Anagram Story

Instructions

This is an anagram puzzle: S_____. The answer to the puzzle is STORY.
       ROTY
Solve the anagrams in this story, and then read the story aloud.

A _____ are quite used to the C_____ of packaged
  SNERICAM   VENONENCIE

products. Some F_____, however, are C_____ by
      RENIGORES   DEFNOUS

them. One day I was having T_____ at the college cafeteria with a
                      AE

S_____ from another C_____. He T_____ open the
  NUTDET   NUTROY   ROE

little tea B_____ and emptied the tea into his C_____. I explained that
    GA   PU

the bag I_____ was meant to be dipped, unopened, into the
    FLETS

W_____. He was S_____ and thanked me for correcting him.
  RATE   RIPEDURS

Then he confidently put an unopened envelope of S_____ into his
                        RAGU

cup of tea.

✎ An Anagram Story

Jack started to work for the XYZ Company in a low paying job. His work

as the _____ was to clean the whole building everyday. However,
ROTIJAN

within six _____ he became a _____. The customers liked him.
SHOTMN   LEMANASS

Within a _____ he became vice-president of the _____. A few months
AREY   COYPAMN

later, the _____ called Jack into his office. He explained that he would
TRESPENID

_____soon and Jack would become president.
TRERIE

Jack said, "_____."
KNATHS

The president asked, "You have been here less than two _____ ,
RAYES

you're already going to be president, and all you can say is thanks?"

"Sorry," Jack replied, "thanks a lot, _____."
ADD

Answers for
the Anagram Stories

#1

theater/theatre
seat
play
enjoy
woman
talking
actors
angry
told
word
business
private

#2

lawyer
call
legs
answered
five
four
tail
make

#3

forget
names
train
forgotten
ticket
told
worry
know
Bishop
without
going

#4

Americans
convenience
foreigners
confused
tea
student
country
tore
bag
cup
itself
water
surprised
sugar

#5

janitor
months
salesman
year
company
president
retire
thanks
years
Dad

Matching Proverbs

Instructions

Instructions

Match the two parts of these proverbs. Draw a line between them. To help you remember the complete proverbs, write them on the lines below.

An apple a day   make light work.

Beggars   make good neighbors.

Many hands   can't be choosers.

April showers   keeps the doctor away.

Good fences   bring May flowers.

1. *An apple a day keeps the doctor away.*

2. _____

3. _____

4. _____

5. _____

SOLO, DUO, TRIO: Puzzles and Games. Reproduced with permission. Copyright © 1997 by Richard Yorkey
Published by PRO LINGUA ASSOCIATES, 15 Elm Street, Brattleboro, Vermont 05301 USA 800 366 4775

Matching Proverbs

Instructions

Match the two parts of these proverbs. Draw a line between them. To help you remember the complete proverbs, write them on the lines below.

If the shoe fits,	beggars would ride.
If you must kick,	wear it.
If you have to whisper,	kick toward the goal.
If something's worth doing,	better not say it.
If wishes were horses,	it's worth doing well.

1. *If the shoe fits, wear it.* _____

2. _____

3. _____

4. _____

5. _____

Matching Proverbs

Don't throw out the baby   in public.

Don't count your chickens   before swine (*pigs*).

Don't put all your eggs   before they hatch.

Don't wash your dirty linen   in one basket.

Don't throw pearls   with the bath water.

1. *Don't throw out the baby with the bath water.*

2. _____

3. _____

4. _____

5. _____

Make hay	before you leap.
Look	until the well runs dry.
Strike	while the sun shines.
You must learn to walk	until trouble troubles you.
Give credit	while the iron is hot.
You never miss the water	before you can run.
Never trouble trouble	where credit is due.

1. *Make hay while the sun shines.*

2. _____

3. _____

4. _____

5. _____

6. _____

7. _____

Matching Proverbs

The early bird   sweeps clean.

A new broom   doesn't grow on trees.

All work and no play   catches the worm.

Children   flies.

Money   finds work for idle hands to do.

The devil   should be seen and not heard.

Time   makes Jack a dull boy.

1. *The early bird catches the worm.*_____

2. _____

3. _____

4. _____

5. _____

6. _____

7. _____

Match the two parts of these proverbs. Draw a line between them. To help you remember the complete proverbs, write them on the lines below.

Half a loaf   is mightier than the sword.

The pen   speak louder than words.

A good name   is better than none.

Actions   the more you want.

The more you get,   is stranger than fiction.

Fact   is as good as a mile.

A miss   is better than gold.

1. *Half a loaf is better than none.*

2. _____

3. _____

4. _____

5. _____

6. _____

7. _____

Matching Proverbs

Instructions

Match the two parts of these proverbs. Draw a line between them. To help you remember the complete proverbs, write them on the lines below.

All that glitters	is lost.
Haste	it pours.
He who hesitates	are soon parted.
A stitch in time	makes waste.
When it rains,	deserves another.
A fool and his money	saves nine.
One good turn	is not gold.

1. _____

2. _____

3. _____

4. _____

5. _____

6. _____

7. _____

SOLO, DUO, TRIO: Puzzles and Games. Reproduced with permission. Copyright © 1997 by Richard Yorkey
Published by PRO LINGUA ASSOCIATES, 15 Elm Street, Brattleboro, Vermont 05301 USA 800 366 4775

Answers for
the Matching Proverbs Puzzles

#1

An apple a day keeps the doctor away.

Beggars can't be choosers.

Many hands make light work.

April showers bring May flowers.

Good fences make good neighbors.

#2

If the shoe fits, wear it.

If you must kick, kick toward the goal.

If you have to whisper, better not say it.

If something's worth doing, it's worth
    doing well.

If wishes were horses, beggars would ride.

#3

Don't throw out the baby with the bath water.

Don't count your chickens before they hatch.

Don't put all your eggs in one basket.

Don't wash your dirty linen in public.

Don't throw pearls before swine.

#4

Make hay while the sun shines.

Look before you leap.

Strike while the iron is hot.

You must learn to walk before you can run.

Give credit where credit is due.

You never miss the water until the well
    runs dry.

Never trouble trouble until trouble
    troubles you.

#5

The early bird catches the worm.

A new broom sweeps clean.

All work and no play makes Jack a dull boy.

Children should be seen and not heard.

Money doesn't grow on trees.

The devil finds work for idle hands to do.

Time flies.

#6

Half a loaf is better than none.

The pen is mightier than the sword.

A good name is better than gold.

Actions speak louder than words.

The more you get, the more you want.

Fact is stranger than fiction.

A miss is as good as a mile.

#7

All that glitters is not gold.

Haste makes waste.

He who hesitates is lost.

A stitch in time saves nine.

When it rains, it pours.

A fool and his money are soon parted.

One good turn deserves another.

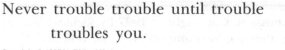

✏️ A Jumbled Story

Instructions

The sentences of this story are jumbled, mixed up. First read them. Then number them in the correct order to tell the story. Then, for writing practice, write the story on the lines below. Check your spelling and punctuation.

○ "See?" his sister told him.

○ She answered, "Because I take smart pills."

○ "They taste like aspirin."

○ "They aren't smart pills," he complained.

○ The brother said, "Give me some smart pills, please."

○ His sister said, "OK. Here, take these two."

○ "You're getting smart already!"

○ A little boy asked his sister, "How come you're so smart?"

_____

_____

_____

_____

_____

_____

SOLO, DUO, TRIO: Puzzles and Games. Reproduced with permission. Copyright © 1997 by Richard Yorkey
Published by PRO LINGUA ASSOCIATES, 15 Elm Street, Brattleboro, Vermont 05301 USA 800 366 4775

A Jumbled Story

Instructions

The sentences of this story are jumbled, mixed up. First read them. Then number them in the correct order to tell the story. Then, for writing practice, write the story on the lines below. Check your spelling and punctuation.

○ The boy shouted, "She called me stupid!"

○ A policeman broke up the battle.

○ The little girl apologized.

○ "What's going on here?" he asked.

○ Why don't you tell him that you're sorry?"

○ The policeman said to the girl, "That isn't very nice.

○ She said, "I'm sorry that you're stupid."

○ Two little kids were having a fist fight in the park.

 # A Jumbled Story

---

Instructions

The sentences of this story are jumbled, mixed up. First read them. Then number them in the correct order to tell the story. Then, for writing practice, write the story on the lines below. Check your spelling and punctuation.

○ "Oh, I'm sorry. I didn't know that you were the mother."

○ Nowadays many boys dress like girls.

○ "Isn't it awful how boys look like girls these days?" I asked.

○ "I'm not. I'm the father."

○ "That's my son," the person answered, pointing to the girl.

○ I turned to the person at the next table.

○ They carry pocketbooks, have long hair, and even wear earrings.

○ One time I was sitting in a restaurant when a girl came in.

SOLO, DUO, TRIO: Puzzles and Games. Reproduced with permission. Copyright © 1997 by Richard Yorkey
Published by PRO LINGUA ASSOCIATES, 15 Elm Street, Brattleboro, Vermont 05301 USA 800 366 4775

✎ A Jumbled Story

#4

Instructions

The sentences of this story are jumbled, mixed up. First read them. Then number them in the correct order to tell the story. Then, for writing practice, write the story on the lines below. Check your spelling and punctuation.

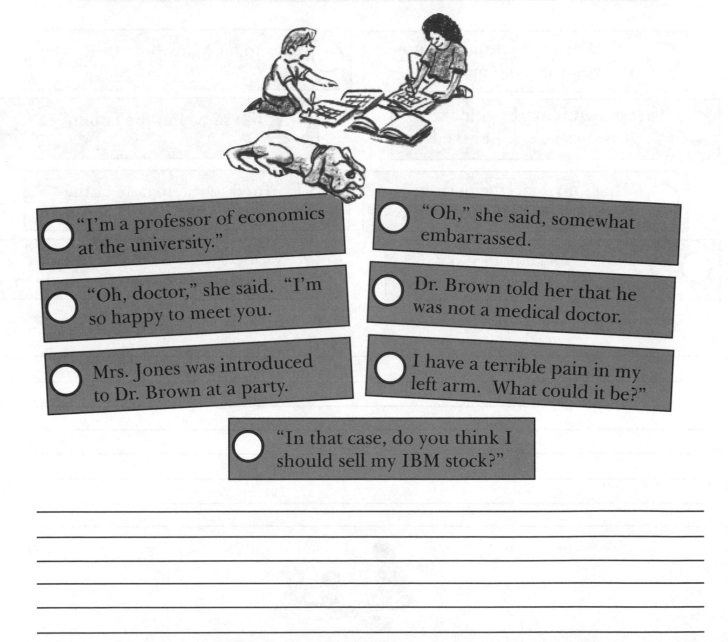

○ "I'm a professor of economics at the university."

○ "Oh," she said, somewhat embarrassed.

○ "Oh, doctor," she said. "I'm so happy to meet you.

○ Dr. Brown told her that he was not a medical doctor.

○ Mrs. Jones was introduced to Dr. Brown at a party.

○ I have a terrible pain in my left arm. What could it be?"

○ "In that case, do you think I should sell my IBM stock?"

_____

_____

_____

_____

_____

_____

Instructions

The sentences of this story are jumbled, mixed up. First read them. Then number them in the correct order to tell the story. Then, for writing practice, write the story on the lines below. Check your spelling and punctuation.

◯ "Why not?" Henry asked.

◯ He would have to have an operation.

◯ The doctor replied, "Yes, it is.

◯ Henry was worried and asked, "Is it a dangerous operation?"

◯ Four out of five people die, but you have nothing to worry about."

◯ A doctor told Henry that he had a serious illness.

◯ "Well, I've already operated on four people and they all died."

_____

_____

_____

_____

_____

_____

Answers for the Jumbled Stories

#1

1. A little boy asked his sister, "How come you're so smart?"
2. She answered, "Because I take smart pills."
3. The brother said, "Give me some smart pills, please."
4. His sister said, "OK. Here, take these two."
5 or 6. "They aren't smart pills," he complained.
6 or 5. "They taste like aspirin."
7. "See?" his sister told him.
8. "You're getting smart already!"

#2

1. Two little kids were having a fist fight in the park.
2. A policeman broke up the battle.
3. "What's going on here?" he asked.
4. The boy shouted, "She called me stupid!"
5. The policeman said to the girl, "That isn't very nice.
6. Why don't you tell him that you're sorry?"
7. The little girl apologized.
8. She said, "I'm sorry that you're stupid."

#3

1. Nowadays many boys dress like girls.
2. They carry pocketbooks, have long hair, and even wear earrings.
3. One time I was sitting in a restaurant when a girl came in.
4. I turned to the person at the next table.
5. "Isn't it awful how boys look like girls these days?" I asked.

6. "That's my son," the person answered, pointing to the girl.
7. "Oh, I'm sorry. I didn't know that you were the mother."
8. "I'm not. I'm the father."

#4

1. Mrs. Jones was introduced to Dr. Brown at a party.
2. "Oh, doctor," she said. "I'm so happy to meet you.
3. I have a terrible pain in my left arm. What could it be?"
4. Dr. Brown told her that he was not a medical doctor.
5. "I'm a professor of economics at the university."
6. "Oh," she said, somewhat embarrassed.
7. "In that case, do you think I should sell my IBM stock?"

#5

1. A doctor told Henry that he had a serious illness.
2. He would have to have an operation.
3. Henry was worried and asked, "Is it a dangerous operation?"
4. The doctor replied, "Yes, it is.
5. Four out of five people die, but you have nothing to worry about."
6. "Why not?" Henry asked.
7. "Well, I've already operated on four people and they all died."

___

Instructions

First read this poem. Use what you know about English spelling, grammar, and punctuation to guess the words. Then, for writing practice, write the poem on the lines below. Check your spelling and punctuation.

I never saw a purple cow

I never hope to see one

But I can tell you anyhow

I'd rather see than be one

___

___

___

___

___

___

Experience is a teacher,

But here's what makes me burn

She always teaches me the things

I do not care to learn

_____

_____

_____

_____

_____

_____

# Top-Half Reading

---

Instructions

First read the following passage. Use what you know about English spelling, grammar, and punctuation to guess the words. Then answer the questions below.

One time Lady Astor and Winston Churchill had an argument. Each became angry, and finally Lady Astor said, "Winston, if I were married to you, I would put poison in your tea."

Churchill immediately answered, "And if I were married to you, I'd drink it!"

I. What are the names of the two people in the story?
_____ and _____

2. Exactly what did the first say to the other?
"_____"

3. Exactly what did the other reply?
"_____"

Women's faults are many:

Men have only two:

Everything they say

And everything they do

1. This poem is about the _____ of both men and women.

2. TRUE or FALSE? Men have only two, so women must have more than men.

   _____

3. What are the two that men have?

   _____

4. Do you agree with the author of this poem? Why or why not?

   _____

   _____

   _____

Instructions

First read the following poem. Use what you know about English spelling, grammar, and punctuation to guess the words. Then answer the questions that follow.

A doctor fell into a well

And broke his collarbone.

The doctor should attend the sick

And leave the well alone.

1. Who is this poem about? _____

2. What happened to him or her? _____

3. What did he or she break? _____

4. What should he or she do? _____

5. Which two words in the poem rhyme? _____ and _____

6. What are the two different meanings here of the word *well*? Is there a third?

    1) _____

    2) _____

    3) _____

Instructions

First read the following quotation. Use what you know about English spelling, grammar, and punctuation to guess the words. Then answer the questions that follow.

"In America, the young are always ready to give to those who are older than themselves the full benefit of their inexperience."

Oscar Wilde

1854   1900

1.   Write the exact words of this quotation.

_____

_____

_____

_____

_____

_____

2.   What's the name of the person who said this? _____

3.   What are the years of his life? _____

Top-Half Reading

Instructions

First read this joke. Use what you know about English spelling, grammar, and punctuation to guess the words. Then answer the questions below.

A businessman was upset because his new secretary was late. When she finally came into the office, he said angrily, "You should have been here at nine o'clock!"

"Why?" she asked. "What happened?"

1. Why was the man angry?

_____

2. What did he say?

_____

3. What was the person's response?

_____

4. Why is this a "humorous" story?

_____

_____

Instructions

First read this amusing story. Use what you know about English spelling, grammar, and punctuation to guess the words. Then answer the questions below.

Sherlock Holmes and Dr. Watson were riding on a train. They passed a large flock of sheep and Watson said "A sizable flock, eh?"

Said Holmes sleepily, "Exactly seven hundred eighty-four in number."

"Good heavens, Holmes!" said Watson. "Surely you can't have counted them all."

"Elementary, my dear Watson," Holmes replied. "I made use of a simple trick that any schoolchild knows. I simply counted the legs and divided by four."

1. What are the names of the two people? _____ and _____

2. Where are they? _____

3. What do they see? _____

4. What number does the second man say? _____

5. What manner does he say it in? _____

6. The first man is surprised. What does he say?_____

7. How does the second man explain his surprising ability? _____

_____

Top-Half Reading

Instructions

First read the following anecdote. Use what you know about English spelling, grammar, and punctuation to guess the words. Then answer the questions below.

Arnold Bennett knew that George Bernard Shaw loved flowers, so he was surprised that there was not a single vase of flowers in his home.

He said, "I thought you were very fond of flowers."

"I am," Shaw replied, "I am very fond of children, too, but I don't chop their heads off and stand them in pots about the house."

1. This story involves two men. What are their names?

   _____ and _____

2. Which one of them was surprised? _____

3. Why? _____

4. Exactly what did the first man say? _____

   _____

5. Exactly what was the other man's reply? _____

   _____

   _____

SOLO, DUO, TRIO: Puzzles and Games. Reproduced with permission. Copyright © 1997 by Richard Yorkey
Published by PRO LINGUA ASSOCIATES, 15 Elm Street, Brattleboro, Vermont 05301 USA 800 366 4775

Answers for the Top-Half Readings

#1

I never saw a purple cow,
I never hope to see one.
But I can tell you anyhow,
I'd rather see than be one.

#2

Experience is a teacher,
But here's what makes me burn.
She always teaches me the things
I do not care to learn.

#3

One time Lady Astor and Winston Churchill had an argument. Each became angry, and finally Lady Astor said, "Winston, if I were married to you, I would put poison in your tea."

Churchill immediately replied, "And if I were married to you, I'd drink it."

1. Lady Astor ... Winston Churchill
2. Winston, if I were married to you, I would put poison in your tea.
3. And if I were married to you, I'd drink it!"

#4

Women's faults are many;
Men have only two:
Everything they say
And everything they do.

1. faults
2. FALSE
3. Everything they say and everything they do.
4. (Whatever you want to write.)

Copyright © 1997 by Richard Yorkey

#5

A doctor fell into a well
And broke his collarbone.
The doctor should attend the sick
And leave the well alone.

1. A doctor.
2. He/She fell into a well.
3. His/Her collarbone.
4. He/She should attend the sick and leave the well alone.
5. *Bone ... alone.* (also *fell ... well*)
6. *(Noun)* A hole in the ground for water. *(Noun)* People who are healthy (or *well*), who are called *the well* as opposed to *the sick. (Adverbial phrase)* To leave something *well enough alone.*

6#

1. "In America, the young are always ready to give to those who are older than themselves the full benefit of their inexperience."
2. Oscar Wilde.
3. 1854 – 1900.

7#

A businessman was upset because his new secretary was late. When she finally came into the office, he said angrily, "You should have been here at nine o'clock!" "Why?" she asked. "What happened?"

1. His new secretary was late.
2. She should have been there at nine.
3. She joked, "Why? What happened?"
4. The secretary interprets *should have been here* to mean *If you had been here, you would have seen something happen.* The businessman means *You ought to have been here* or *You were obliged to be here.*

8#

Sherlock Holmes and Dr. Watson were riding on a train.

They passed a large flock of sheep and Watson said, "A sizable flock, eh?" Said Holmes sleepily, "Exactly seven hundred eighty-four in number." "Good heavens, Holmes!" said Watson. "Surely you can't have counted them all." "Elementary, my dear Watson," Holmes replied. "I made use of a simple trick that any schoolchild knows. I simply counted the legs and divided by four."

1. Sherlock Holmes ... Doctor Watson
2. On a train.
3. A large (sizable) flock of sheep.
4. 784.
5. Sleepily.
6. "Good heavens, Holmes!..."
7. He says he made use of a simple trick that any schoolchild knows. He simply counted the legs and divided by four.

#9

Arnold Bennett knew that George Bernard Shaw loved flowers, so he was surprised that there was not a single vase of flowers in his home.

He said, "I thought you were very fond of flowers."

"I am," Shaw replied. "I am very fond of children, too, but I don't chop their heads off and stand them in pots about the house."

1. Arnold Bennett ... George Bernard Shaw.
2. Arnold Bennett.
3. There was not a single vase of flowers in Shaw's home.
4. "I thought you were very fond of flowers."
5. "I am. I am very fond of children, too, but I don't chop their heads off and stand them in pots about the house."

A

rage attorney consumes 17 trees of paper each year

MIAMI, Fla. (AP) – The average attourney files, faxes, and photocopies a lot of paper ach year. According to one estimate, each tourney comsumes 17 trees. Florida h ut 50,000 lawyers. So about 800. become lawyer's paper each yea

B

MERICA'S FUNNIEST EOS (In Stereo) *9336285*
8:00 pm
❷ ㊶ ㊻ NOVA (In Stereo) (CC) *4285 40339 99049*
tereo)
EN (In ❸ ③ ❹ ❻ PRIMARY COVERAGE (In Stereo) (CC) *1339 97223 2681 22339*
6827
IR (In ❺ ❽ ❿ ㊵ ROSEANNE (In Stereo) (CC) *4117 7827 8575 977575*
⑤ BLOSSOM (In Stereo) (CC) *41407*
ORT ⑦ BARETTA *401223*
❼ ⑬ ㉛ WINGS (In Stereo) (CC)
9285 3049 13759
MOVIE: PLATOON LEA
(CC)
Stere
(In S

C

SENSE & SENSIBILITY (PG)
6:55 & 9:15
MATINEE 2 P.M. EVERYDAY

BROKEN ARROW (R)
7 & 9:10
NO MATINEES

MR. HOLLAND'S OPUS (PG)
6:45 & 9:20
MATINEE 2 P.M. EVERYDAY

DUNSTON CHECKS IN (PG)
MATINEE 2 P.M. EVERYDAY

D

pension and has scanner in vehicle.

8:19 a.m., accident, Putney Road.

8:36 a.m., assist Vermont State Police on I-91.

9:59 a.m., subject arrested for aggravated assault and attempted murder, bail $100,000, Putney Road.

10:08 a.m., check on welfare of person, Canal Street.

10:44 a.m., cows loose from farm and are in roadway, Bonnyvale Road.

11:43 a.m., accident, Main Street.

11:49 a.m., daughter was scratched by stray cat, Canal Street.

11:51 a.m., vandalism to building, eggs thrown against it, Moore Court.

1:28 p.m., alarm, human error, Main Street.

E

AKC BEAGLES, 4-1/2 years old. Female, $300. Spayed female, $150. Both good rabbit dogs. Call evenings 6-9 p.m. 413-665-3711.

LLAMAS, ALPACAS - for fun, pets, backpackers, spinners. Many available, pictures, brochures. West Mountain Farm, Inc., Stamford, VT 05352. 802-694-1417.

PURRR-FECT VALENTINES. CFA Persian kittens, 9 weeks, shots, many colors, $250. Older kittens. Domestic and Persian stud service available. 802-694-1219.

TRACTORS: Farmall A, rebuilt engine, many new parts, $1100. EQUIPMENT: John Deere 8 ft. transport harrows, $1050. New Idea 9 ft. haybine, $850. 8 ft. cultipacker, $250. Farmall A, BN, C, H, M, 460 tractors for parts. Kolakoski Farm, 1 mile off Rt. 5, North Hillside Road, across from Candlelight Restaurant, So. Deerfield, MA 01373, 413-665-3009.

MAPLE SUGARING EQUIPMENT - quantity used sap buckets, 3-1/2 x 8 steam hood, sap pumps, filter tank, 3-300 gal. sap tanks, other misc.

F

Mailbox No. 11940
Passionate, Athletic, Intelligent
DWF, 5'3", 124 lbs, 49, NS. ISO DWM, 46+, who likes outdoors, movies, fine dining, music, adventure, and travel. Voice Mailbox No. 11910

Petite SWF
Mother of one ISO SWM with great sense of humor and lots of energy. I enjoy traveling, espresso, and having fun. Voice Mailbox No. 11929

S/DWF, 32, 5'3", 128 lbs.
Enjoys quiet times, dancing, fishing, camping, and is a mother of two. ISO sincere, honest friendship with a single male, 30-35, for a possible relationship. Voice Mailbox No. 11888

Abominable Snowman
It's an abomination to be so single! Celibate New Age monk sick of hibernating. One foot in the real world. SWM, 42, ISO monkess, any description. All replies answered. Voice Mailbox No. 11890

Adventurous, Honest SM
ISO SF, 18-35, who's honest, sincere, and has a deep sense of moral values. Enjoys reading, movies, concerts, traveling, and working out at the gym. Voice Mailbox No. 11960

Bellows Falls Area
SWM, mid 40s, 6', 175 lbs, sensitive, sincere, easygoing, NS, ND. Seeks attractive SWF for fun, conversation, friendship, maybe more. Voice Mailbox No. 11949

Bi WM, 40, ISO Bi WM, 18-32

1. _____ News article   2. _____ Police log   3. _____ Personals
4. _____ Movie listing   5. _____ TV listing   6. _____ Classified ads

---

SOLO, DUO, TRIO: Puzzles and Games. Reproduced with permission. Copyright © 1997 by Richard Yorkey
Published by PRO LINGUA ASSOCIATES, 15 Elm Street, Brattleboro, Vermont 05301 USA 800 366 4775

What Are You Reading? #2

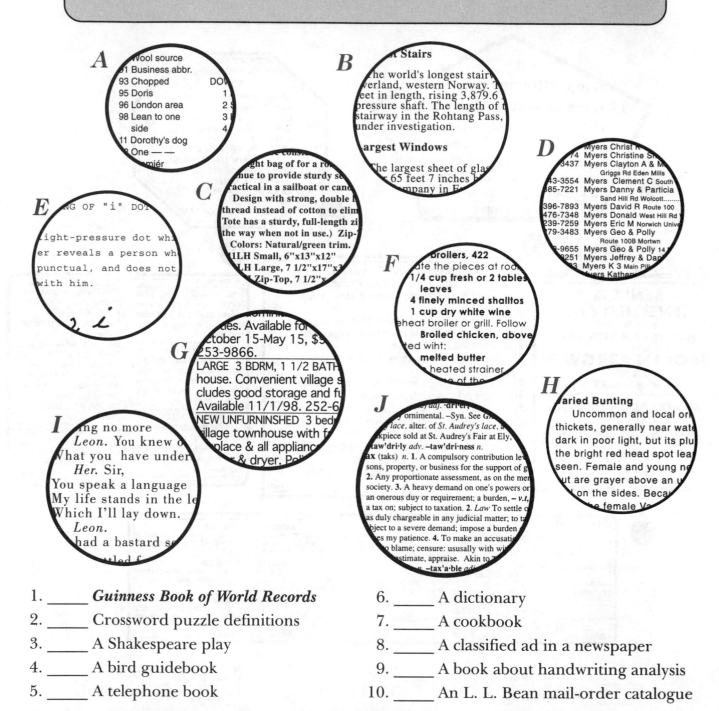

Match the sample reading material in the circles with the sources listed below.

A
Wool source
91 Business abbr.
93 Chopped   DO
95 Doris   1
96 London area   2
98 Lean to one   3
   side   4
11 Dorothy's dog
  One — —
  _emiér

B
st Stairs

The world's longest stair
verland, western Norway. T
eet in length, rising 3,879.6
pressure shaft. The length of t
stairway in the Rohtang Pass,
under investigation.

argest Windows

The largest sheet of glas
r 65 feet 7 inches
mpany in E

C
e const
ght bag of for a ro
nue to provide sturdy se
actical in a sailboat or cand
Design with strong, double
thread instead of cotton to elim
Tote has a sturdy, full-length zi
the way when not in use.) Zip-
Colors: Natural/green trim.
1LH Small, 6"x13"x12"
LH Large, 7 1/2"x17"x3
Zip-Top, 7 1/2"x

D
Myers Christ
74 Myers Christine S
3437 Myers Clayton A & M
        Griggs Rd Eden Mills
43-3554 Myers Clement C South
85-7221 Myers Danny & Particia
        Sand Hill Rd Wolcott........
396-7893 Myers David R Route 100
476-7348 Myers Donald West Hill Rd
239-7259 Myers Eric M Norwich Unive
79-3483 Myers Geo & Polly
        Route 100B Mortwn
9-9655 Myers Geo & Polly 14
251 Myers Jeffrey & Dan
3 Myers K 3 Main Pil
yers Kathe

E
NG OF "i" DOT

ight-pressure dot wh
er reveals a person wh
punctual, and does not
with him.

F
broilers, 422
te the pieces at ro
1/4 cup fresh or 2 tables
     leaves
4 finely minced shalltos
1 cup dry white wine
eheat broiler or grill. Follow
     Broiled chicken, above
ed wiht:
     melted butter
     heated strainer
     e of the

G
es. Available for
ctober 15-May 15, $9
253-9866.

LARGE 3 BDRM, 1 1/2 BATH
house. Convenient village s
cludes good storage and fu
Available 11/1/98. 252-6
NEW UNFURNINSHED 3 bed
illage townhouse with f
place & all applianc
r & dryer. Pol

H
aried Bunting
Uncommon and local or
thickets, generally near wate
dark in poor light, but its plu
the bright red head spot lea
seen. Female and young n
ut are grayer above an u
l on the sides. Beca
e female Va

I
ing no more
   Leon. You knew
What you have under
   Her. Sir,
You speak a language
My life stands in the le
Which I'll lay down.
   Leon.
   had a bastard s
   ttled f

J
aj. drive
y ornamental. –Syn. See G
lace, alter. of *St. Audrey's lace,*
kpiece sold at St. Audrey's Fair at Ely,
aw'dri·ly *adv.* –taw'dri·ness *n.*
ax (taks) *n.* **1.** A compulsory contribution le
sons, property, or business for the support of g
2. Any proportionate assessment, as on the me
society. **3.** A heavy demand on one's powers or
an onerous duy or requirement; a burden, – *v.t,*
a tax on; subject to taxation. **2.** *Law* To settle o
as duly chargeable in any judicial matter; to ta
bject to a severe demand; impose a burden
es my patience. **4.** To make an accusati
o blame; censure: ususally with wi
stimate, appraise. Akin to ?
–tax'a·ble *adj*

1. _____ *Guinness Book of World Records*
2. _____ Crossword puzzle definitions
3. _____ A Shakespeare play
4. _____ A bird guidebook
5. _____ A telephone book
6. _____ A dictionary
7. _____ A cookbook
8. _____ A classified ad in a newspaper
9. _____ A book about handwriting analysis
10. _____ An L. L. Bean mail-order catalogue

SOLO, DUO, TRIO: Puzzles and Games. Reproduced with permission. Copyright © 1997 by Richard Yorkey
Published by PRO LINGUA ASSOCIATES, 15 Elm Street, Brattleboro, Vermont 05301 USA 800 366 4775

✎ What Are You Reading? #3

Instructions

On this page and the next there are samples of ten different kinds of reading material. Write the letter for each sample next to the phrase in the list below that identifies it. There are twelve phrases, so you won't use two of them. Put an X next to these.

1. _____ A murder mystery

2. _____ A weather report

3. _____ A mutual fund invest-

      ment report

4. _____ A historical novel

5. _____ A zodiac, or astrological

      horoscope

6. _____ A how-to manual

7. _____ A romantic love story

8. _____ A religious novel

9. _____ A joke book

10. _____ A science fiction story

11. _____ A legal document

12. _____ A medical journal

A

asking more decisions, as defined.

Statutes Annotated, Title 14, Chapter 121.

    2. <u>Specific Powers</u>. The general grant shall include, but not be limited to, the followi

      a. <u>Possession and Management of Reale</u> enter upon and take possession of any lands of bu tenements or other structures, or any parts there be rated, that now or hereafter may belong to the whereof I am or may be entitled.

Any and all buildings, tenements, or other stru

B

...ch Home Safety Kits comes packaged with t. Sonic Siren Smoke Alarum. Also included are: two (2) plastic screw achors, two (2) 1 3/4 incl wood screws, and a plastic mounting bracket.

    To install your Sonic Siren Smoke Alarum

    1. Remove the mounting bracket from the alarum unit.

    2. Fasten the mounting bracket to the ceiling with the screws provided. (See illustra tion.) If possible, sink screws into a ceiling joist. I joist cannot be located, plastic anchors (supplied should be used. Susing a pencil, hold the mountin bracket in the desired location and mark the ceilin through the screw holes. Drill a 3/16th inch hol through the markings and puch or tap in the an chors. Mounting plate can now be secured with th screws. (Molly fasteners or toggle bolts may als be used to secure the plate.) Be sure the mountin plate is securely attached to the ceiling.

    3. Install the batteries in the battery ...lder under the lid of the Sonic Siren Smok

---

C

After Port Lowell he's among fire eating twice sparkplug
He agreed that *no* one on Earth would make him change h
mind. They had reckoned without someone from Mars.

The Red Planet was no longer quite so red, thoug
he process of greening it had barely begun. Concentra
ng on the problems of survival, the colonists (they hate
he word and were already saying proudly "we Martians"
had little energy left over for art or science. But the ligh
ning flash of genius strikes where it will, and the greate
heoretical physicist of the century was born under th
bubble domes of Port Lowell.

D

appening. Tiberius held the bridges but d
not attempt to cross the Rhine not havin
confidence yet in his troops, whom he wa
busy knocking into shape. The German
did not attempt to cross either. Augustu
grew impatient again with Tiberius, an
urged him to avenge Varus without furthe
delay and win back the lost Eagles. Tiberiu
answered that nothing was nearer to h
own heart, but that his troops were not ye
fit to attempt the task. Augustus sent ou
Germanicus when he had finished his ter
of magistracy, and Tiberius then had t
show some activity. He was not really laz
or a coward, only extremely cautious. H
crossed the Rhine and then overran par
of the lost province.

E

Research continued throughout the next six months. But it was not
ny more than insulin is a "cure" for diabetes, and, like diabetes
rheumatism could only be kept in hand as long as regular injection
of Compound E were given. As soon as the injections stopped, th
patients relapsed into their previous condition, the more miserabl
in fact because of the temporary well-being they had experienced.

It was then found that similar effects could be obtained by mean
of another hormone, ACTH, or Adreno-Cortico-Tropic Hormone
obtained from the anterior lobe of the pituitary, or hypophysis, gland
which controls the adrenals. Remove it and the gland that has rev

G

Two gentlemen, both hard of hearing and strangers to each other were
about to ride the London Underground. One of them, peering at the
station they were entering, said, "Pardon me, sir, but is this Wembley?"

"No," said the other, "Thursday."

"No, thank you," said the first, "I've already had my little drink."

F

It was obvious that Anna worked at it, systematically
She had a pretty face, and her sleazy white dress clung
provocatively to her' youthful body, its tiny shoulder strap
showing an expanse of decolletage. Her hand, with its
outrageously long silver fingernails, kept intwining itself
in Lyon's. She hung onto his words. She tossed her hair
At one point she said something and Lyon threw back his
head and laughed. Then he leaned over and planted a quick
kiss on the tip of her nose. Anna felt passionately, vitally

H

during the 12 months ended July 31. It
marked the 18th consecutive fiscal year
that an investment in IFA, with dividends
reinvested, has increased in value. IFA is
one of only a handful of equity mutual
funds that have been able to demonstrate
such consistency over this extended period.

Your Fund also outpaced the leading
unmanaged stock and bond market indi-
ces during the fiscal year over the 12
months Standard & Poor's 500 Composite
Index gained 12.8% on a reinvested basis

I

hating Arden - but they did not kill him. All of you Cloade
had a motive for killing Rosaleen Cloade and yet none o
you killed her. This case is, always has been, *the wrong
way round*. Rosaleen Cloade was killed by the person
who had *most to lose* by her death.' He turned his head
slightly, 'You killed her, Mr Hunter . . .'

'I?' David cried. 'Why on earth should I kill my twin
sister?'

'You killed her because she wasn't what she seemed

J

generally optimistic, you often possess a bright, cheery smile that warms th
hearts of those around you. While sometimes tactless, you are without guile
and what comes into the head slips right out of the mouth (unless Scorpio pre
dominates elsewhere in your chart).

You should work in a job or career that allows you to pioneer something
new or encourages you to be independent. You are very capable around people

✎ What Are You Reading? #4

A

plans strict new air s

By LAURA MECKLER
The Associated Press

WASHINGTON – In a victory for environmentalists, the Environmental Protection Agency will propose tougher air quality standards Wednesday that could force many cities to impose costly pollution controls and change many Americans' lifestyles.

The EPA plans to toughen restrictions for ozone levels by a third and, for the first time, regu-e minute particles of dust in the administration

the source, who spoke on the condition that he not be identified.

The EPA has scheduled a press conference for Wednesday to announce the proposal, which must go through a months-long review before it can become law.

The plan is likely to be hotly debated in Congress, which could overturn the rules under a new law that seeks to protect small businesses. The Clean Air Act self also is up for renewal

The rules also

B

ssociation player
"And I really haven't s
at all season long."
Gilliam mean by giddy?
a couple of corny jokes,"
plained. "Nobody laughed.
ned like he was thrilled to
yhow."
reason to be thrilled. The
is team (22-29) are riding a
inning streak, their longest
o seasons and the longest in
eign.
for No. 5 here Wednes-
st the Bucks, who are
nternal dissension relat-
tar forward Vin Baker's
nt with some of his team-

ts might not need help. By
ce the All-Star break, they
tely talk about the playoffs
ot fear anybody laughing at

are coming together as a
e post-Derrick Coleman
Anderson era.
his second season at the
ed today after practi
ncis, Wis

An
us.'.

This
seem a
were a
P. J. Br
scrimmag
Deion Sand
"You ap
when you win
is in his third N
to practice, you
tice becomes a le
faster. You don't
big fun. Like the fe
when we were winni
playoffs. We had a p
that year and we're sta
feeling back."
Which is o

C

leeper omlinson

STOWE – Mabel Sleeper Tomlinson, 94, died Tuesday, Oct. 22, 1996, in Morrisville.

She was born in Stowe on Aug. 17, 1902, the daughter of Edward and Flora Shepard Sleeper. She was a 1921 graduate of Stowe High School.

She married Cletus Tomlinson ctober 1921. He predeceased 1977. Mrs. Tomlinson and d far

of the
Sickle Cha
munity Churc
Stowe Woman's
member of the
Church until th
Community Church
She is survived I
C.Floyd of Seymou
S.of Lansing, Mich
Stowe; one da
Tromble
N.Y

1. _____ **A movie review**
2. _____ **A weather report**
3. _____ **A letter to the editor**
4. _____ **An obituary**
5. _____ **A travel article**
6. _____ **An editorial**
7. _____ **A headline article**
8. _____ **A real estate listing**
9. _____ **A wedding announcement**
10. _____ **A sports story**

[1]

...at Anthony was leav-...
...ree man.
...would still be news to Didg-
...C. Wilson), Anthony's madly
...friend. Didgnan looks on through
...oculars while Anthony makes a showy
concession to his friend's sense of high
drama. Anthony leaves his room by slipping
out the window, even though this baffles a
doctor who has come to see him off. "Look
how excited he is!" explains Anthony, pointing to his friend in the underbrush nearby.
With that, "Bottle Rocket" declares i...
...wn boyishness, which is as d...
...nan's and sometim...

...Texas college friend,...
minute black-and-white shor...
...ed to a brightly colored family affair t...
ing three Wilson brothers in acting role...
"Bottle Rocket" makes the most of its taste
for self-deluding adolescent games.
A mildly facetious tone limits Mr. Ande...
son's film to the lightweight, but the coll...
tive enthusiasm behind this debut effort s...
comes through. What's best about "Bo...
Rocket" is not the laid-back pranks
inflate its story to feature length b...
offbeat élan with which that stor...
The big-sky minimalism of the f...
...ttractively spare...

[7] Buy, but n...

Columnists Donella Meadows and Robert
Lawson both recently advocated on this page
that the people of this region buy nothing on
Friday, Nov. 29 – historically the busiest
shopping day of the Christmas season – to
support Planetary Buy Nothing Day.
The idea of a Buy Nothing Day started in
1992 in Canada as a way to protest "consum-
erism" and to get people to realize that the
world's natural resources must be shared
among all its citizens. It is now also celebrated
the United States, England, Ireland, th
therlands, Australia and New Zealand.
According to one of the advertisem...
...ced by The Media Foundation in (...
...ting the day, "the average N...
...nsumes five times m...
...imes more th...

[3]

...rt behind. Tem-
...o 10 degrees above
...the region.
...k near the eastern
...chians from Virgin-
...w clouds and
...r sections

...vers in West Virg...
eastern Kentucky. Colder, moist air will
cover much of the upper Ohio Valley
and western Great Lakes. Freezing rain
will glaze parts of northern Michigan
while a few flurries dust the ground of
eastern Wisconsin.
The Plains will... mild as

Heavy
tain snows w...
of colder air in
Showers will
across the No...
ies. Snow sh...
...western...

[6]

...y the early 1990's, two-thirds
building was vacant.
The Mendik Company and Qua...
...m Realty Partners, which togethe...
...wn half the building (Columbia Uni-
...versity owns the other half), are
...utting $40 million into renovating
...nd marketing it.
Kevin R. Wang, senior vice president at Mendik, said the building was
about a quarter leased. "There are
also leases pending on the 6th and
7th floors and on half the 10th," Mr.
Wang said. "And we're talking to
...everal restaurant people about th...
...r storefront."
...investment com...

[5] Reflections on the 'battle of century'

Editor of the Reformer:
The last boxing match I watched
was between Ali and Frazer. To
this little boy, these men were
gargantuan, two titans battling
over the Universe.
As I grew, I saw boxing as
something ridiculous and une-
volved. It wasn't a bloody struggle
over meat in the Serengeti. It
wasn't a border dispute. It wasn't
someone protecting his wife and
children from a swinging blade.
It was two men (and now
women) choosing to hurt one another for that kind of money.
I had no interest in watching this
bloodsport. Until the other night,
when Evander Holyfield stepped
into the ring with Mike Tyson.
Something told me this fight was
going to be about something more
than boxing. It was.
For weeks, the media hyped the
...atch as "Finally!"

...asked Holy...
boxing and how h...
Tyson, he could only t...
faith and that it was Go...
that brought down Goliath.
Don King, hair and all, stood
proudly by Holyfield, his new
money machine.
And there was poor Tyson in the
corner, bewildered and shaken, a
shadow of a man hunched over on
a stool.
His entourage bickering and
shuffling this way and that with
their zoot suits, Stetson's and la-
pelled flowers, probably wonder--
ing when they should approach
Holyfield, their new guru.
Emptiness surrounded Tyson.
But, something came out of him
that I didn't expect – humility.
"He's a great fighter, and I take
my hat off to him," Tyson said of
Holyfield's victory.
Could the man inside the killi...
machine we built finally see '
self, his own life and plac...
universe?
Staring...

What Are You Reading?

A

"I wonder, Miss Dove," he said, "if you'd give me a check for five hundred pounds payable to Mrs. Percival Fortescue."

He had the pleasure of seeing Mary Dove lose countenance for once.

"The silly fool told you, I suppose," she said.

"Yes. Blackmail, Miss Dove, is rather a serious charge."

"It wasn't exactly blackmail, Inspector. I think you'd find it hard to make out a case of blackmail against me. I was just doing Mrs. Percival a special service to oblige her."

"Well, if you'll give me that check, Miss Dove, we'll leave it like that."

Mary Dove got her checkbook and took out her fountain pen.

B

When you look back on it, you used to lead a sheltered life. Your employer took care of your pension, life insurance and medical plan. Saving meant putting money in a bank. Social Security took up the slack.

Now the world has changed. You're alone in the woods, and you think there may be bears.

That's where MetLife comes in.

1. _____ A poem

2. _____ A book review

3. _____ A magazine advertisement

4. _____ A historical novel

5. _____ An encyclopedia

6. _____ A mystery story

7. _____ A science fiction novel

8. _____ A nursery rhyme

9. _____ A Western

10. _____ A memoir

SOLO, DUO, TRIO: Puzzles and Games. Reproduced with permission. Copyright © 1997 by Richard Yorkey
Published by PRO LINGUA ASSOCIATES, 15 Elm Street, Brattleboro, Vermont 05301 USA 800 366 4775

The foremost ship was the *Franklin*, an American privateer of twenty-two guns, nine-pounders, and her pursuer was the *Surprise*, a twenty-eight-gun frigate formerly belonging to the Royal Navy but now acting as a privateer too, manned by privateersmen and volunteers: she was nominally commanded by a half-pay officer named Thomas Pullings but in fact by her former captain, Jack Aubrey, a man much higher on the post-captain's list than would ordinarily have been found in so small and antiquated a ship – an anomalous craft entirely, for although she purported to be a privateer her official though unpublished status was that of His Majesty's Hired Vessel *Surprise*. She had set out on her voyage with the purpose of carrying her surgeon, Stephen Maturin, to South America, there to enter into contact with those leading inhabitants who wished to make Chile and Peru independent of Spain: for Maturin, as well as being a doctor of medicine, was an intelligence-agent exceptionally well qualified for this task, being a Catalan on his mother's side and bitterly opposed to Spanish – that is to say Castilian – oppression of his country.

Sing a song of six pence, a pocket full of rye,
Four and twenty black birds baked in a pie.
When the pie was opened, the birds began to sing.
Oh, wasn't that a dainty dish to set before the king.

The king was in his counting house, counting out his money,
The queen was in the parlor eating bread and honey,
And maid was in the garden hanging out the clothes
When along came a black bird and snipped off her nose.

Pipher's view—and what, no doubt, helps make her work so popular—is that, for the most part, the culture, not the parents, are to blame. Pipher points out that girls enter junior high school faced with daunting magazine and movie images of glossy, thin, perfect women. She argues that pop culture is saturated with sex; violence against women is rampant; and drugs and alcohol are far more ac-

History. Most of the area that is now Hungary and TRAN-SYLVANIA was conquered in the late 9th cent. A.D. by the MAGYARS, a Finno-Ugric people from beyond the Urals; Christianization was completed by St. STEPHEN (r.1001–38), first king of Hungary. A feudal society developed, con-trolled by a few powerful nobles, the magnates. Hungary was ruled after 1308 by the Angevin dynasty and after 1386 by other foreign houses. In 1526 the Ottoman Turks de-feated the Hungarians at the battle of Mohács. In the long wars that followed the Turks dominated most of Hungary, while Transylvania was ruled by noble families (see BÁTHORY and RÁKÓCZY). By 1711, however, all Hungary had fallen un-der HAPSBURG control. A short-lived independent Hungarian republic (1849) under Louis KOSSUTH was overthrown by Austrian and Russian troops, and in 1867 the AUSTRO-HUN-GARIAN MONARCHY was established, in which Austria and Hungary were nearly equal partners. After the collapse of the Dual Monarchy in WORLD WAR I, Hungary was pro-claimed (1918) an independent republic and drastically re-

It was many and many a year ago
In a kingdom by the sea,
That a maiden there lived,
    whom you might know
By the name of Annabel Lee.
And this maiden she lived
    with no other thought
But to love, and be loved by me.

I particularly regretted leaving the Buffalo Soldiers project unfinished. I had been able to light a fire under it, and I did not want that fire to go out. I had a black civilian on my staff whom I trusted implicitly, Alonzo Dougherty, who was also an officer in the Kansas National Guard. "Lonnie," I said, "you know what this project means to me. I'm turning it over to you. I'll continue to do whatever I can, long distance. But I am counting on you to keep it alive here." Dougherty agreed to carry on.

SOLO, DUO, TRIO: Puzzles and Games. Reproduced with permission. Copyright © 1997 by Richard Yorkey
Published by PRO LINGUA ASSOCIATES, 15 Elm Street, Brattleboro, Vermont 05301 USA 800 366 4775

Instructions

Match the sample reading material in the boxes with the sources listed below.

a

PRODUCT NO.	UPC CODE	COLOR	SHEET SIZE	LIST PRICE
SPR 05120	0 35255 00504	White	8½"x11"	9.90 PK
SPR 05121	0 35255 00505	Blue	8½"x11"	10.64 PK
SPR 05122	0 35255 00506	Canary	8½"x11"	10.64 PK
SPR 05123	0 35255 00507	Green	8½"x11"	10.64 PK
SPR 05124	0 35255 00508	Pink	8½"x11"	10.64 PK
SPR 05125	0 35255 00805	Goldenrod	8½"x11"	10.64 PK

b

45	46	47
Rh Rhodium 102.9055	**Pd** Palladium 106.42	**Ag** Silver 107.8682
2 . 8 . 18 16 . 1	2 . 8 . 18 18 . 0	2 . 8 . 18 18 . 1
77	78	79
Ir Iridium 192.2	**Pt** Platinum 195.08	**Au** Gold 196.9665
2 . 8 . 18 32 . 15 . 2	2 . 8 . 18 32 . 16 . 2	2 . 8 . 18 32 . 18 . 1

c

▶ Nursing Homes

BUCKLEY NURSING HOME
95 Laurel Greenfield Ma ----------**413 774-3143**
Country Village Community Care Home
Bellows Falls Vt ----------**800 286-4720**
CRESCENT MANOR NURSING HOME
Crescent Blvd Bennington ----------**447-1501**
HARBORSIDE HEALTHCARE-APPLEWOOD
Snow Rd Winchester ----------**603 239-6355**
LINDEN LODGE
75 Linden Brat ----------**258-3704**

d

Rank	City, Country	Pop. (thousands) 1994	Pop. (thousands, projected) 2015	Annual growth rate (percent) 1990-1995	Percentage increase between: 1975-1995	1995-2015
1.	Tokyo, Japan	26,518	28,700	1.4	35.7	7.0
2.	New York City, U.S.	16,271	17,600	0.3	2.8	8.0
3.	Sao Paulo, Brazil	16,110	20,800	2.0	66.0	26.6
4.	Mexico City, Mexico	15,525	18,800	0.7	39.2	20.1
5.	Shanghai, China	14,709	23,400	2.3	31.8	55.0
6.	Bombay, India	14,496	27,400	4.2	120.1	81.4
7.	Los Angeles, U.S.	12,232	14,300	1.6	39.0	15.0
8.	Beijing, China	12,030	19,400	2.6	44.7	57.1
9.	Calcutta, India	11,485	17,600	1.7	48.0	51.0
10.	Seoul, South Korea	11,451	13,100	1.9	71.2	12.9
11.	Jakarta, Indonesia	11,017	21,200	4.4	138.9	84.1

e

EASTERN CONFERENCE	Atlantic Division								
	W	L	Pct	GB	L10	Streak	Home	Away	Conf
Orlando	37	14	.725	—	7-3	Won 3	27-0	10-14	21-9
Knicks	31	18	.633	5	7-3	Lost 1	19-8	12-10	20-12
Washington	23	28	.451	14	3-7	Lost 1	16-9	7-19	11-22
Miami	23	29	.442	14½	4-6	Lost 2	16-11	7-18	13-18
Nets	22	29	.431	15	5-5	Won 4	15-8	7-21	16-16

f

Time Difference

China 86 .... **+13**
Beijing (Peking) 1
Guangzhou (Canton) 20
Shanghai 21
Colombia 57 .... **0**
Bogota 1
Costa Rica* 506 .... **-1**
Cyprus 357 .... **+7**
Czech Republic 42 .... **+6**

g

Weight Not Over			
(lb.)	(oz.)	Canada¹	Mexico
0	0.5	$ 0.46	$ 0.40
0	1	0.52	0.46
0	1.5	0.64	0.66
0	2	0.72	0.86

i

Bahamas	809
Bermuda	809
California	
Fresno	209
Los Angeles	213
Los Angeles	310

h

United Mcgill Harwood Hill Benn **442-8536**
UNITED STATES GOVERNMENT—
 AGRICULTURE DEPT—
 Agriculture Stabilization & Conservation County Committee
 118 South St Benn **447-7595**
 Agricultural Stabilization & Conservation Serv
 78 Center Ptfd **413 443-9227**
 Agricultural Stabilization & Conservation Service
 257 South Main Rutl **775-8034**
 Farmers Home Adm
 118 South St Benn **442-3169**
 Forest Service Dist
 Routes 11 & 30 Man **362-2307**
 Soil Conservation Serv South St Benn .. **442-2275**
COURTS—
 Fedl Court Judge Gagliardi—
 Route 7A Man **362-5786**

j

Bennington College	.05201
Benson	.05731
Bethel	.05032
Bolton Valley	.05477
Bomoseen	.05732
Bondville	.05340
Bradford	.05033
Brandon	.05733
Brattleboro	.05301

k

28³/₄	21¹¹/₃₂	Sonco n	.60y	2.2	16	639	27⁷/₈	27⁵/₈	27³/₄ − 1/8
61	51¹/₄	Sonco pfA n2.25	3.8	...	4	59¹/₈	59¹/₈	59¹/₈ − 1/4
66¹/₄	42¹/₂	**SonyCp**	.45o	0.8	...	568	59¹/₄	58³/₈	58³/₈ −2¹/₂
15⁵/₈	10³/₈	Sothbys	.32	2.2	36	564	14⁷/₈	14⁵/₈	14⁷/₈ + 1/8
45⁷/₈	39	SourcCp	3.70h	8.3	q	27	45	44³/₈	44³/₈ − 5/8
29³/₄	26³/₄	SourcCp pf2.40	8.3	...	15	29	29	29	...
26³/₄	22¹/₈	SrcOM pfA2.11	8.1	...	13	26¹/₈	26	26 − 1/4
27	25¹/₈	SrcOM	...	...	...	41	26³/₄	26	26¹/₄

l

Manila	84/75	*	88/ 70
Martinique	84/72	.09	84/ 70
Merida	93/64	0	84/ 63
Mexico City	76/52	0	70/ 43
Montego Bay	86/70	0	84/ 72
Monterrey	95/66	0	72/ 52
Montreal	40/25	.10	27/ 10
Moscow	26/16	trc	25/ 14
Nairobi	85/57	0	79/ 55
Nassau	76/57	0	77/ 64

1. _____ Zip Code listing
2. _____ NY Stock Exchange listing
3. _____ Office supply catalogue
4. _____ Telephone book White Pages
5. _____ Weather report
6. _____ Postal rate chart
7. _____ N.B.A. (basketball) standings
8. _____ International calling codes
9. _____ Periodic table
10. _____ World Almanac chart
11. _____ Area Code listing
12. _____ The Yellow Pages

Answers for
What Are You Reading?

#1
1. A
2. D
3. F
4. C
5. B
6. E

#2
1. B
2. A
3. I
4. H
5. D
6. J
7. F
8. G
9. E
10. C

#3
1. I
2. X
3. H
4. D
5. J
6. B
7. F
8. X
9. G
10. C
11. A
12. E

#4
1. D
2. E
3. G
4. C
5. X
6. F
7. A
8. H
9. X
10. B

#5
1. G
2. E
3. B
4. C
5. F
6. A
7. X
8. D
9. X
10. H

#6
1. J
2. K
3. A
4. H
5. L
6. G
7. E
8. F
9. B
10. D
11. I
12. C

✏️ A Word Search Puzzle #1

#1

Instructions

The following names of **fruits and vegetables** are hidden in this puzzle, either horizontally [⇨] or vertically [⇩]. First find and circle each of the words.

APPLE	CORN	LIME	PEACH
CELERY	GRAPE	ORANGE	PUMPKIN
CHERRY	LEMON	PEAS	TOMATO

```
O A P P L E T C
R C U C E P O U
A O L I M E M C
N R M G O A A H
G N B R N S T E
E P E A C H O R
P U M P K I N R
E R C E L E R Y
```

Now read the leftover letters in order, left to right and top to bottom, and you will find the name of another vegetable. Write each letter on the lines below.

___ ___ ___ ___ ___ ___ ___ ___ ___

SOLO, DUO, TRIO: Puzzles and Games. Reproduced with permission. Copyright © 1997 by Richard Yorkey
Published by PRO LINGUA ASSOCIATES, 15 Elm Street, Brattleboro, Vermont 05301 USA 800 366 4775

✏️ A Word Search Puzzle #2

Instructions

The following words used to talk about **lunchtime** in the U.S. are hidden in this puzzle, in these four directions [⇨ ⇩ ⬈ ⬊]. First find and circle each of the words.

~~BAGEL~~	DONUT	JELLO®	MILK	SODA
~~BAG LUNCH~~	FAST FOOD	JUICE	SANDWICH	SOUP
DESSERT	FRUIT	LUNCHBOX	SNACK	THERMOS®

```
L M F R U I T A A D
U T I L U N C D S E
N H B L H E O D N S
C E A A K S O O A S
H R G N G O O M C E
B M E E F L S E K R
O O L T L T U O I T
X S S E N D O N U T
G A J J U I C E C P
F S A N D W I C H H
```

Note: JELLO® and THERMOS® are registered brand names and must always be printed with the reistration mark ®.

Now read the leftover letters in order, left to right and top to bottom, and you will learn what business people do when they want to have lunch with another business person.

They have __   _____ _____.

SOLO, DUO, TRIO: Puzzles and Games. Reproduced with permission. Copyright © 1997 by Richard Yorkey
Published by PRO LINGUA ASSOCIATES, 15 Elm Street, Brattleboro, Vermont 05301 USA 800 366 4775

✎ A Word Search Puzzle #3

BEANS	FISH	PIE	SALAD
BREAD	HAMBURGER	PIZZA	SPAGHETTI
CAKE	MILK	POTATO	STEAK
CHICKEN	PEAS	~~RICE~~	WINE

```
F P S A L A D K I S
H I I Y O U L T N E
P A S E C I T A C P
O A M H M E E I W I
T N T B H B R A I Z
A K E G U B P P N Z
T O A E T R R E E A
O P K L U C G E A K
S A S T E A K E A S
C C H I C K E N R D
```

Now read the leftover letters in order, and you will learn an informal dinner invitation:
"Please come to dinner. I have nothing fancy planned, but –

___ ___ ___ – ___ ___ ___ ___ ___ ___ ___ ___ ___ ___ ___ ___."

✎ A Word Search Puzzle #4

SOLO, DUO, TRIO: Puzzles and Games. Reproduced with permission. Copyright © 1997 by Richard Yorkey
Published by PRO LINGUA ASSOCIATES, 15 Elm Street, Brattleboro, Vermont 05301 USA 800 366 4775

Instructions

The names of the following **breakfast foods** are hidden in this puzzle, in these four directions [⇨ ⇩ ⬃ ⬀]. First find and circle each of the words.

BACON   FRENCH TOAST   JUICE   SAUSAGE
CEREAL   FRUIT   MILK   SYRUP
COCOA   HAM   MUFFINS   TEA
COFFEE   HONEY   PANCAKES
EGGS   ~~JAM~~   PASTRIES

```
B  E  M  U  F  F  I  N  S  A  T
P  A  G  T  A  C  O  N  O  S  Y
A  C  C  G  E  T  I  C  A  E  C
S  O  P  O  S  A  O  O  N  S  E
T  F  N  A  N  C  T  O  E  Y  R
R  F  N  T  N  H  H  A  L  R  E
I  E  B  R  C  C  F  E  A  U  A
E  E  M  N  K  K  A  R  H  P  L
S  A  E  L  F  A  S  K  U  A  T
J  R  I  J  U  I  C  E  E  I  M
F  M  S  A  U  S  A  G  E  S  T
```

Now read the leftover letters in order, left to right and top to bottom, and you will find out what Americans call a simple breakfast of coffee and toast.

___ ____ ____ ____ ____ ____ ____ ____

A Word Search Puzzle #5

Instructions

The names of the following kinds of **household furnishings** are hidden in this puzzle, in these three directions [⇨ ⇩ ⬂]. First find and circle each of the words.

~~BED~~	CRIB	OVEN	SINK
CHAIR	CUPBOARD	RADIO	TABLE
CLOCK	DESK	REFRIGERATOR	TOILET
COT	FREEZER	RUG	
COUCH	FIREPLACE	SHOWER	

```
R E F R I G E R A T O R
T F I I M C E A R O V C
S B R T R O R D U I E U
C H E E F E I I G L N P
C O O D E X P O B E S B
H L U W C Z T L H T I O
A E O C E O E C A L N A
I O C C H R T R K C K R
R D E S K T A B L E E D
```

Now read the leftover letters in order, and you will find the answer to this riddle:
When the clock says it's 25, what time is it?

It's _____ _____ _____ _____ _____!

SOLO, DUO, TRIO: Puzzles and Games. Reproduced with permission. Copyright © 1997 by Richard Yorkey
Published by PRO LINGUA ASSOCIATES, 15 Elm Street, Brattleboro, Vermont 05301 USA 800 366 4775

A Word Search Puzzle #6

BASEBALL	FOOTBALL	PING-PONG	SKIING
BOXING	GOLF	POLO	SOCCER
DIVING	HOCKEY	POOL	TENNIS

```
S  O  C  C  E  R  F  P  L
G  P  I  N  G  P  O  N  G
O  A  D  B  Y  I  O  N  G
L  G  I  O  A  M  T  E  H
F  S  V  X  I  S  B  F  O
S  K  I  I  N  G  A  P  C
T  E  N  N  I  S  L  O  K
U  N  G  G  P  O  L  O  E
B  A  S  E  B  A  L  L  Y
```

Now circle the leftover letters. Those letters, in order, will spell out a four-word sentence about sports. Write the sentence on the lines below:

_ _ _ _ _ _ _ _ _   _ _ _ _ _ _   _ _   _ _ _ _!

✏️ A Word Search Puzzle

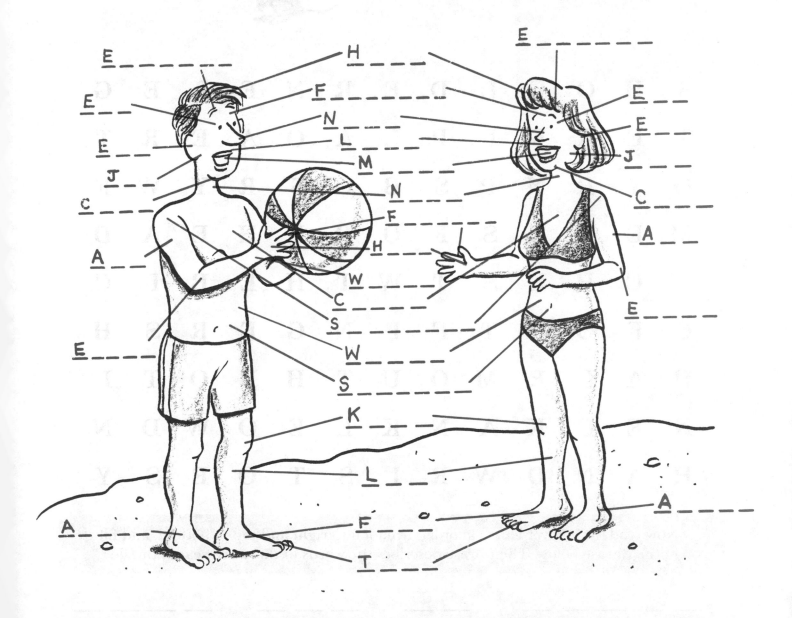

SOLO, DUO, TRIO: Puzzles and Games. Reproduced with permission. Copyright © 1997 by Richard Yorkey
Published by PRO LINGUA ASSOCIATES, 15 Elm Street, Brattleboro, Vermont 05301 USA 800 366 4775

```
S H O U L D E R N E L E G
T E A K I P L A O A E R T
O Y R N P S B O S R Y W F
M E M E S F O R E H E A D
A C H E S T W T H E B I C
C F O O T F I N G E R S H
H A I R M O U T H B O T I
N E C K A N K L E O W D N
H A N D W R I S T O E S Y
```

Now read the leftover letters in order, from left to right and top to bottom, and fill in the phrase below. The phrase describes the words in this word search puzzle.

___ ___ ___ ___ ___ ___   ___ ___   ___ ___ ___ ___ ___ ___ ___ ___

✎ A Word Search Puzzle #8

Instructions

You need the following words to talk about **school**. They're hidden in this puzzle, in these four directions [↗ ↘ ⇩ ⇦]. First find and circle each of the words.

CLASS   HOMEWORK   PROFESSOR   STUDENTS

COURSE   LECTURE   SUBJECT   TEXTBOOK

HISTORY   LIBRARY   SCHEDULE   TUTOR

```
P A T E X T B O O K
S R L E C T U R E Y
T C O S K A T K R S
U L T F E C R O T C
D A A C E O T H U H
E S E J W S R F T E
N S B E I O S R O D
T U M H H E L O R U
S O C O U R S E R L
H L I B R A R Y P E
```

Now read the leftover letters in order, and they will spell out some good advice.
What's the best thing to do if you don't understand something in school?

__ __ __ __ _ __ __ __ __ __ __ __ __ __ __ .

A Word Search Puzzle #9

BAT	DEER	FOX	LION	MOUSE	OX
BEE	EEL	GOOSE	LOON	MULE	TURTLE
CLAM	FISH	HORSE	MONKEY	OWL	WHALE

```
M O N K E Y B G L
O A H S O O A O O
U F O A X W T O O
S I R M U L E S N
E S S P B E E E E
A H E L I O N F C
T U R T L E O O E
C K W H A L E X E
D E E R C L A M L
```

Now read the leftover letters in order, and they will complete this phrase:

As proud __ __   __   __ __ __ __ __ __ __ __

This is a simile. A simile is an expression that compares two things, using the words *like* or *as*.

Using the names of the the animals in the puzzle, complete each of these common similes:

1. as strong as an __ __

2. as blind as a __ __ __

3. as busy as a __ __ __

4. as slippery as an __ __ __

5. as sly as a __ __ __

6. as wise as an __ __ __

7. as brave as a __ __ __ __

8. as crazy as a __ __ __ __

9. as happy as a __ __ __ __

10. as stubborn as a __ __ __ __

11. swims like a __ __ __ __

12. runs like a __ __ __ __

13. eats like a __ __ __ __ __

14. as big as a __ __ __ __ __

15. as quiet as a __ __ __ __ __

16. as silly as a __ __ __ __ __

17. as slow as a __ __ __ __ __ __

18. climbs like a __ __ __ __ __ __

✏ A Word Search Puzzle #10

AIRPLANE	BUS	MOTORCYCLE	TAXI
AUTO	CAMEL	RAFT	TRICYCLE
AUTOMOBILE	CAR	ROLLERSKATES	TROLLEY
BICYCLE	CART	SHIP	VAN
BOAT	LIMOUSINE	SUBMARINE	YACHT

```
T A U T O M O B I L E S
R R U S M O E O S I A U
O C I T L T L A H M I B
L A B C O O A T I O R M
L M I Y Y R G X P U P A
E E C Y A C V R I S L R
Y L Y R A Y L A B I A I
A B C A G C E E N N N N
C U L F T L H R U E E E
A S E T C E K T C A R T
R O L L E R S K A T E S
```

Now read the leftover letters in order, and you will find the answer to this riddle:
What has four wheels and flies?

It's a _ _ _ _ _ _ _ _ _ _ _ _ _ _ _ _ _ _ _ _.

A Word Search Puzzle #11

ANTENNA	FLAT TIRE	JACK	ROOF
BRAKE	GAS CAN	KEY	SEATBELT
BUMPER	GAS CAP	LICENSE	STEERING WHEEL
CAR	HEADLIGHT	LOCK	TRUNK
DOOR	HOOD	LUGGAGE	WHEEL
DRIVER	HORN	PARKING LIGHTS	WINDOW
FENDER	HUBCAP	PASSENGER	WINDSHIELD

```
A P F P A S S E N G E R L R
G N A E J W I N D O W E E L
S A T R N A H O R N E V E F
H S S E K D C E A H I E D L
E E T C N I E K W R H O B A
A A E L A N N R D W O L Y T
D T R O T P A G G H S E S T
L B O C A P E N L T K V C I
I E O K A S I N B I R E A R
G L F C N R A L D U G U R E
H T B E E C I V E O M H N S
T U C E S B R E A K O P T K
H I T A L U G G A G E R E S
L S G W I N D S H I E L D R
```

Now read the leftover letters in order, from left to right and top to bottom, and you will learn something that every driver should know:

_ _!

SOLO, DUO, TRIO: Puzzles and Games. Reproduced with permission. Copyright © 1997 by Richard Yorkey
Published by PRO LINGUA ASSOCIATES, 15 Elm Street, Brattleboro, Vermont 05301 USA 800 366 4775

Instructions

The following words that are all related to **money and banking** are hidden in this puzzle, in these four directions [⇨ ⇩ ⬃ ⬈]. First find and circle each of the words.

ACCOUNT	BORROW	DEBIT	LOAN
AGENT	BROKER	DEPOSIT	MORTGAGE
ASSET	CASH	DIVIDEND	PAY
ATM	CHARGE	DOLLAR	SAVINGS
BALANCE	CHECK	INSURANCE	STATEMENT
BANK	COD (CASH ON DELIVERY)	INTEREST	STOCK
BILL	COINS	INVOICE	TELLER
BOND	CREDIT	LIABILITY	WITHDRAWAL

```
B A C S T A T E M E N T E S D
S R G H B A N K M A R C L N E
I T O E E B I L L E N A E G S
M N O K N C T P C A W D R N U
O T S C E T K I L A I A I S O
R M P U K R O A R V H O D E M
T O A N R V B D I C C E E Y T
G C Y A N A H D S C S I B L E
A A D I T T N A D A R E I O L
G S F E I W R C C E V E T A L
E H S W O A O C E C P I D N E
R S A R L A T M O R O O N I R
A A R L B O N D I D N U S G T
Y O O D I N T E R E S T N I S
B D A Y L I A B I L I T Y T T
```

Now read the leftover letters in order and get some good advice.

Be _ _ _ _ _ _ . _ _ _ _ _ _ _ _ _ _ _ _

_ _ _ _ _ _ _ _ _ _ _ _ _ _ _ _ _ .

A Word Search Puzzle #13

Instructions

For each of the following verbs, the *past tense* form is hidden in this puzzle, either horizontally [⇨] or vertically [⇩]. First find and circle each of the words. Some of the words overlap. Two are done as examples.

BEGIN	EAT	HEAR	SHOOT	STRIKE	THROW
BRING	GET	KNOW	SING	TAKE	WIN
CUT	GROW	PUT	SPEND	TEACH	
	HANG	SEND	STEAL	THINK	

```
S  C  S  T  O  L  E  A  S
P  U  T  H  E  A  R  D  T
E  B  R  O  U  G  H  T  R
N  U  G  U  H  O  U  K  U
T  A  U  G  H  T  N  N  C
O  T  S  H  O  T  G  E  K
O  E  A  T  H  R  E  W  C
K  T  N  G  R  E  W  O  U
B  E  G  A  N  S  E  N  T
```

Now read the leftover letters in order, from left to right and top to bottom, and you will find that they spell the past tense of another irregular verb.

_____ _____ _____ _____ _____

SOLO, DUO, TRIO: Puzzles and Games. Reproduced with permission. Copyright © 1997 by Richard Yorkey
Published by PRO LINGUA ASSOCIATES, 15 Elm Street, Brattleboro, Vermont 05301 USA 800 366 4775

54

A Word Search Puzzle #14

Instructions

For each of the following verbs, the *past participle* form is hidden in this puzzle, in these four directions [⇨ ⇩ ⬂ ⬈]. First find and circle each of the words.

BREAK	FALL	GO	RING	SINK	SWIM
BUY	FEED	GROW	RISE	SPEAK	TAKE
DRAW	FIND	LAY	SAY	SPREAD	TEAR
DRINK	FORGIVE	READ	SING	STEAL	WRITE

```
D L Y O S P R E A D E N
R R A R I S E N U N W D
S U U I V E R N O A A D
T T N N D W E G R E I I
O O S G K V R D R A E N
L R T O I T B I S T H S
E N E G H N S R T C H W
N A R G E D G P O T L U
L O U L N K S R O K E M
F O L U N E N U O K E N
B A O U F E D G N W E N
F F S T A K E N E G N N
```

Now read the leftover letters in order, and fill in the spaces below.
If you have done something difficult, what have you done?

__ __ __ __ , __ __ __ __ __ __ __ __ __ __ __

__ __ __ __ __ __ __ __ __ __ __ __ __ __ !

A Word Search Puzzle #15

CHILD	GOOSE	LEAF	MOOSE	SERIES	THIEF
DEER	HALF	LIFE	MOUSE	SHEEP	WIFE
FOOT	HOOF	LOAF	OX	SHELF	WOLF
FISH	KNIFE	MAN	SELF	TOOTH	WOMAN

```
L G D S E R I E S T S S
K O E E M I C E E E E S
H N A E E G O E V V E S
C A I V S R F I L V E O
S H L V E E L E A V D H
S H I V E S S E O E T T
H W E L E S L O S E F H
E O W E D S H O E N I I
L L F I P R O T E I S E
V V M S V M E M H I H V
E E E N T E O N H E S E
S S N E A W S O X E N S
```

"There are lots of _ _ _ _ _ _ _ _ _ _ _ _ _ _ _ _ _ _ _."

SOLO, DUO, TRIO: Puzzles and Games. Reproduced with permission. Copyright © 1997 by Richard Yorkey
Published by PRO LINGUA ASSOCIATES, 15 Elm Street, Brattleboro, Vermont 05301 USA 800 366 4775

Answers for the Word Search Puzzles

#1
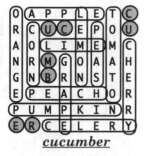
cucumber

#2
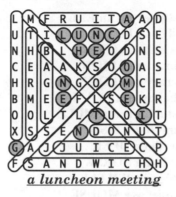
a luncheon meeting

#3
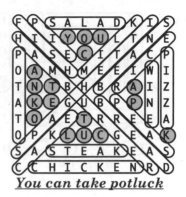
You can take potluck

#4
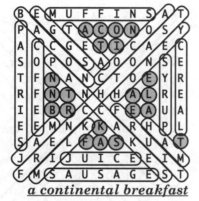
a continental breakfast

#5
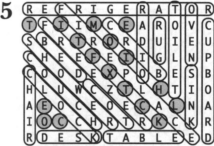
time to fix the clock

#6

Playing games is fun!

#7
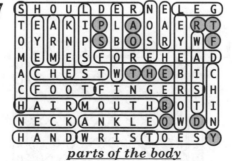
parts of the body

#8
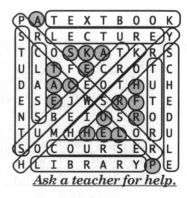
Ask a teacher for help.

Answers for
the Word Search Puzzles

#9

as proud as a peacock

1. as strong as an OX
2. as blind as a BAT
3. as busy as a BEE
4. as slippery as an EEL
5. as sly as a FOX
6. as wise as an OWL
7. as brave as a LION
8. as crazy as a LOON
9. as happy as a CLAM
10. as stubborn as a MULE
11. swims like a FISH
12. runs like a DEER
13. eats like a HORSE
14. as big as a WHALE
15. as quiet as a MOUSE
16. as silly as a GOOSE
17. as slow as a TURTLE
18. climbs like a MONKEY

#10

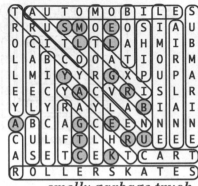

smelly garbage truck

#11

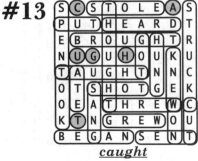

Seatbelts save lives

#12

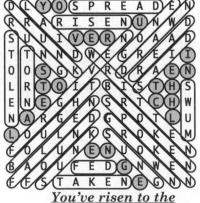

*(Be) smart. Put some money aside
for a rainy day.*

#13

S C S T O L E A S
P U T H E A R D T
E B R O U G H T R
N U G U H O U K U
T A U G H T N N C
O T S H O T G E K
O E A T H R E W C
K T N G R E W O U
B E G A N S E N T

caught

#14

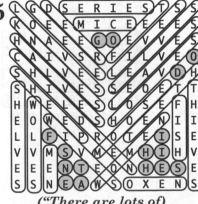

You've risen to the challenge!

#15

("There are lots of) good fish in the sea."

✎ A Crossword Puzzle #1

#1

Instructions

The subject of this crossword puzzle is **colors**. Fill in the puzzle with the names of the colors listed below.

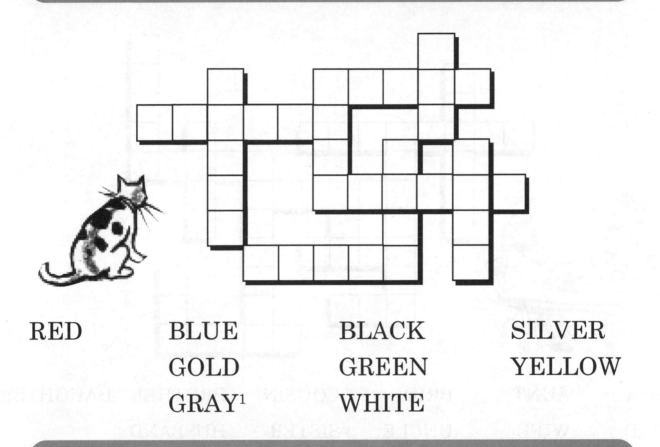

RED	BLUE	BLACK	SILVER
	GOLD	GREEN	YELLOW
	GRAY[1]	WHITE	

Now write the names of at least four other colors that are not used in this puzzle.

_____

_____

_____

_____

[1] In British English, this word is spelled <u>grey</u>.

Instructions

The subject of this crossword puzzle is **family relationships**. Fill in the puzzle with the names of the family members listed below.

SON	AUNT	BRIDE	COUSIN	BROTHER	DAUGHTER
DAD	WIFE	UNCLE	SISTER	HUSBAND	
MOM		GROOM			

Now arrange the words in common pairs. One is already done for you. What one word doesn't fit the pattern? Why not?

_____*mom*_____and_____*dad*_____   _____and_____

_____and_____   _____and_____

_____and_____   _____and_____

✏ A Crossword Puzzle

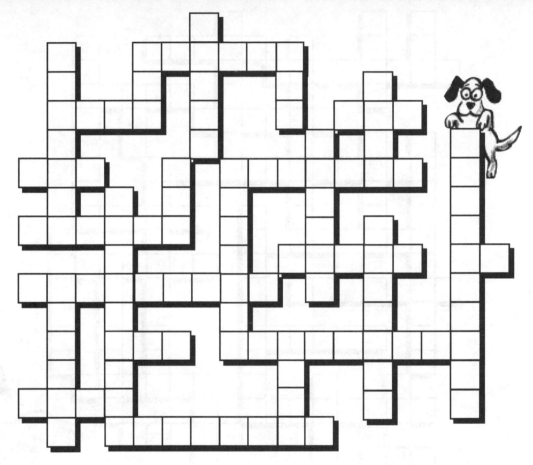

OX	APE	FROG	TIGER	COYOTE	BUFFALO	ELEPHANT
	CAT	LION	SNAKE	DONKEY	GORILLA	ALLIGATOR
	COW	LOON		RABBIT	GIRAFFE	CROCODILE
	DOG	WOLF		RACOON[1]	LEOPARD	PORCUPINE
	PIG					RHINOCEROS
	YAK					

[1] Also spelled <u>raccoon</u>.

SOLO, DUO, TRIO: Puzzles and Games. Reproduced with permission. Copyright © 1997 by Richard Yorkey
Published by **PRO LINGUA ASSOCIATES**, 15 Elm Street, Brattleboro, Vermont 05301 USA 800 366 4775

A Crossword Puzzle

Instructions

Below this crossword puzzle is a list of **occupations**. Use a dictionary to define any that you are not sure of. Then fit each word into its place in the puzzle.

SPY	MAID	MASON	DOCTOR	PAINTER	ENGINEER	SECRETARY
NUN	COOK	ACTOR	WRITER	JANITOR	MINISTER	ARCHITECT
VET		PILOT	ARTIST	SURGEON	SURVEYOR	
		MOVER	PRIEST	TEACHER	DIPLOMAT	JOURNALIST
		NURSE	BANKER			TECHNICIAN
		BAKER				TRANSLATOR
		SKIER				RECEPTIONIST

SOLO, DUO, TRIO: Puzzles and Games. Reproduced with permission. Copyright © 1997 by Richard Yorkey
Published by **PRO LINGUA ASSOCIATES**, 15 Elm Street, Brattleboro, Vermont 05301 USA 800 366 4775

A Crossword Puzzle #5

BAY	CAVE	DELTA	VALLEY	EQUATOR	LATITUDE	WATERFALL
SEA	HILL	SOUTH	DESERT	VOLCANO	MOUNTAIN	LONGITUDE
	EAST	RIVER	STREAM	PLATEAU		
	WEST	COAST				
	GULF	PLAIN				
	LAKE	BEACH				
	COVE	NORTH				

✎ A Crossword Puzzle

Instructions

Each of the words below this puzzle is a noun that expresses some kind of **feeling or emotion.** Use a dictionary to look up any words you don't know. Then fit each word into its place in the puzzle.

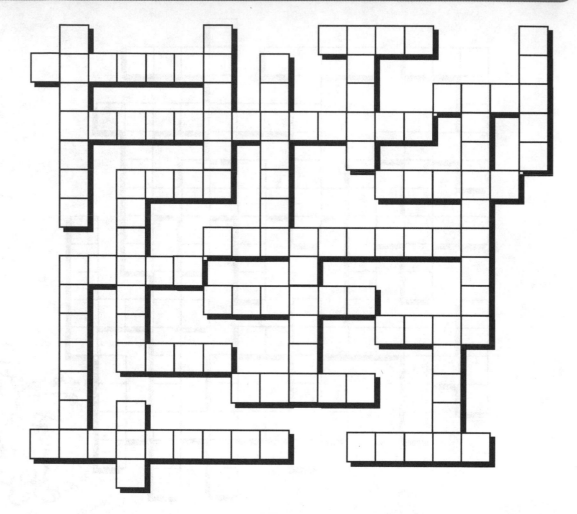

JOY	ENVY	ANGER	HORROR	BOREDOM	AMUSEMENT	ENTHUSIASM
	FEAR	BLISS	REGRET	COURAGE	ANNOYANCE	
	HATE	GREED	TERROR	DISGUST		EMBARRASSMENT
	LUST	GRIEF		FATIGUE		
	RAGE	PRIDE		PASSION		
		SHAME				
		WORRY				

SOLO, DUO, TRIO: Puzzles and Games. Reproduced with permission. Copyright © 1997 by Richard Yorkey
Published by PRO LINGUA ASSOCIATES, 15 Elm Street, Brattleboro, Vermont 05301 USA 800 366 4775

A Crossword Puzzle

Instructions

Can you match each of the countries in this puzzle with its capital? Below, write the number of the capital on the line before the name of the country. Try to guess before you use an atlas or a dictionary. Can you find these countries on a map?

___ Algeria   ___ Ecuador   ___ Libya   ___ Sudan

___ Australia   ___ Guatemala   ___ Luxembourg   ___ Switzerland

___ Austria   ___ Haiti   ___ Nepal   ___ Syria

___ Belgium   ___ India   ___ Norway   ___ Tunisia

___ Brazil   ___ Japan   ___ Peru   ___ Venezuela

___ Burma   ___ Laos   ___ Somalia   ___ Zaire

___ China   ___ Liberia   ___ Spain   ___ Zimbabwe

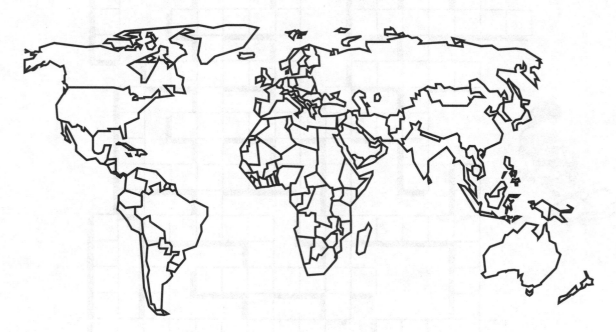

1. Algiers   8. Damascus   15. Luxembourgville   22. Quito

2. Beijing   9. Guatemala City   16. Madrid   23. Rangoon

3. Bern   10. Harare   17. Mogadishu   24. Tokyo

4. Brasilia   11. Khartoum   18. Monrovia   25. Tripoli

5. Brussels   12. Katmandu   19. New Delhi   26. Tunis

6. Canberra   13. Kinshasa   20. Oslo   27. Vienna

7. Caracas   14. Lima   21. Port-au-Prince   28. Vientiane

A Crossword Puzzle

The subject of this crossword puzzle is **languages**. Fill in the puzzle with the names of the languages listed below.

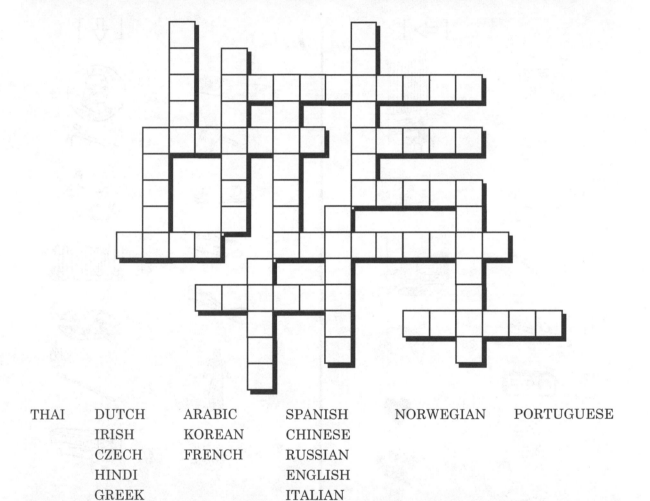

THAI	DUTCH	ARABIC	SPANISH	NORWEGIAN	PORTUGUESE
	IRISH	KOREAN	CHINESE		
	CZECH	FRENCH	RUSSIAN		
	HINDI		ENGLISH		
	GREEK		ITALIAN		

Now write the name of the language commonly spoken in each of these countries.

1. Thailand _____   5. Greece _____   9. Holland _____   13. France _____

2. Russia _____   6. Australia _____   10. Korea _____   14. Ireland _____

3. Italy _____   7. China _____   11. India _____   15. Spain _____

4. Saudi Arabia _____   8. Portugal _____   12. Norway _____   16. Czech Republic _____

✎ A Crossword Puzzle

Instructions

This is a **vocabulary builder** crossword puzzle using 34 **nouns**. Write the name of each object (the noun) in the correct place on the puzzle on the next page.

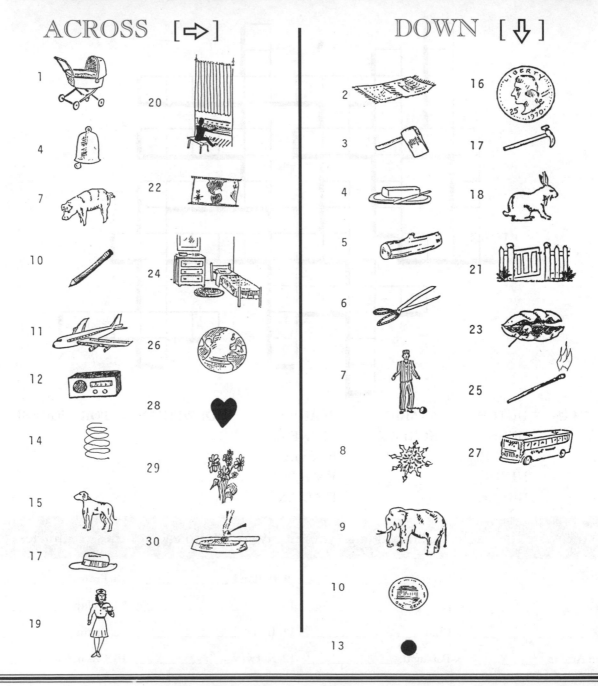

Instructions

Write the 34 **nouns** (the names of the objects pictured on the other page) in the correct places on this vocabulary builder crossword puzzle. Match the numbers and directions on the picture page with those on the puzzle below. For example, the name of object 1 starts in square 1 and goes *across* 8 spaces – the noun has 8 letters. The name for object 2 goes *down* 3 spaces. There are two objects numbered 4. One goes *across* 4 spaces, the other *down* 6 spaces.

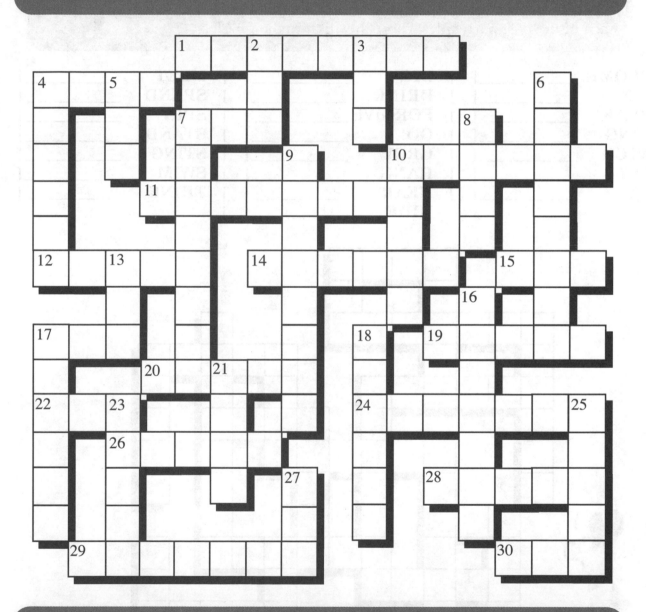

When you have finished this **noun builder** puzzle, take a piece of paper and write a funny short story using as many of these nouns as you can.

Published by PRO LINGUA ASSOCIATES, 15 Elm Street, Brattleboro, Vermont 05301 USA 800 366 4775

✎ A Crossword Puzzle

Instructions

To solve this puzzle, write the **past participle forms** of the verbs listed below on the lines next to the verbs. Then write the number of letters in each word between the brackets – [ ]. Finally, using the number of letters to help you, place each of the past participles where they fit into the puzzle.

BECOME _____ [ ]   DIG _____ [ ]   MEET _____ [ ]
BITE _____ [ ]   DRINK _____ [ ]   SPEND _____ [ ]
BREAK _____ [ ]   FORGIVE _____ [ ]   SPIN _____ [ ]
BRING _____ [ ]   GO _____ [ ]   STAND _____ [ ]
CATCH _____ [ ]   GROW _____ [ ]   STING _____ [ ]
COST _____ [ ]   HANG _____ [ ]   SWIM _____ [ ]
CUT _____ [ ]   HEAR _____ [ ]   THINK _____ [ ]
                        HIDE _____ [ ]

A Crossword Puzzle

ACROSS [⇒]

2. fight	13. catch	22. cut
6. oversleep	15. take	24. tell
9. put	16. rebuild	26. cost
10. win	19. keep	29. remake
11. sit	20. dig	30. mean

DOWN [⇩]

1. bring	7. sing	21. get
2. flee	8. think	23. hurt
3. teach	12. strike	25. lead
4. understand	14. write	27. see
5. go	17. leave	28. swim
	18. hold	

A Crossword Puzzle

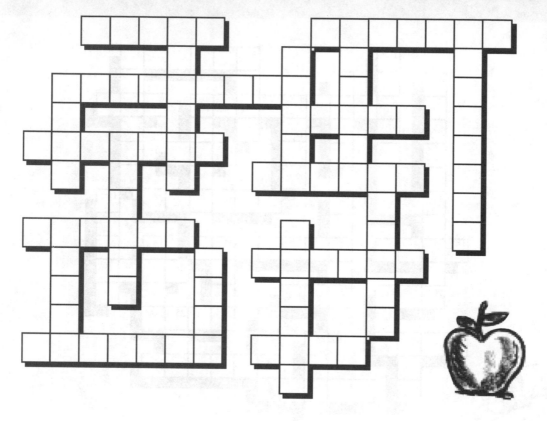

CORN	APPLE	BANANA	CABBAGE	CUCUMBER
LIME	OLIVE	CARROT	LETTUCE	
PEAS	ONION	CHERRY	SPINACH	PINEAPPLE
	PEACH	ORANGE		
		PEPPER		
		RADISH		
		RAISIN		
		TOMATO		

SOLO, DUO, TRIO: Puzzles and Games. Reproduced with permission. Copyright © 1997 by Richard Yorkey
Published by PRO LINGUA ASSOCIATES, 15 Elm Street, Brattleboro, Vermont 05301 USA 800 366 4775

A Crossword Puzzle

Instructions

The subject of this crossword puzzle is **restaurants**. Fill in the puzzle with the words listed below, all of which have something to do with dining at a restaurant.

TAX	BOWL	CHECK	BUFFET	SERVING
TEA	CHEF	PLATE	COURSE	
TIP	DISH	SALAD	ENTREE	TABLECLOTH
	FORK	TABLE	NAPKIN	
	MEAL		WAITER	RESERVATION
	MENU			

A Crossword Puzzle

ARM	CHIN	ANKLE	FINGER	STOMACH
EYE	HAND	CHEST	THROAT	
JAW	HEAD	ELBOW	TONGUE	
LEG	NECK	MOUTH		
RIB		THIGH		
TOE		THUMB		
		WAIST		
		WRIST		

Instructions

First label the **parts of the body** used in the puzzle. Add the names of other body
parts you know or want to learn. Then answer the questions at the bottom of
the page. The answer to the last question is some good advice for everyone.

#14

What is the man doing?									WEIGHTS
What is the dog doing?									GOOD DOG!
What is the woman doing?									SO GRACEFULLY
*What should we all do?**	STAY						WITH SPORTS

Hint: the answer is given in the three outlined squares above.

Answers for the Crossword Puzzles

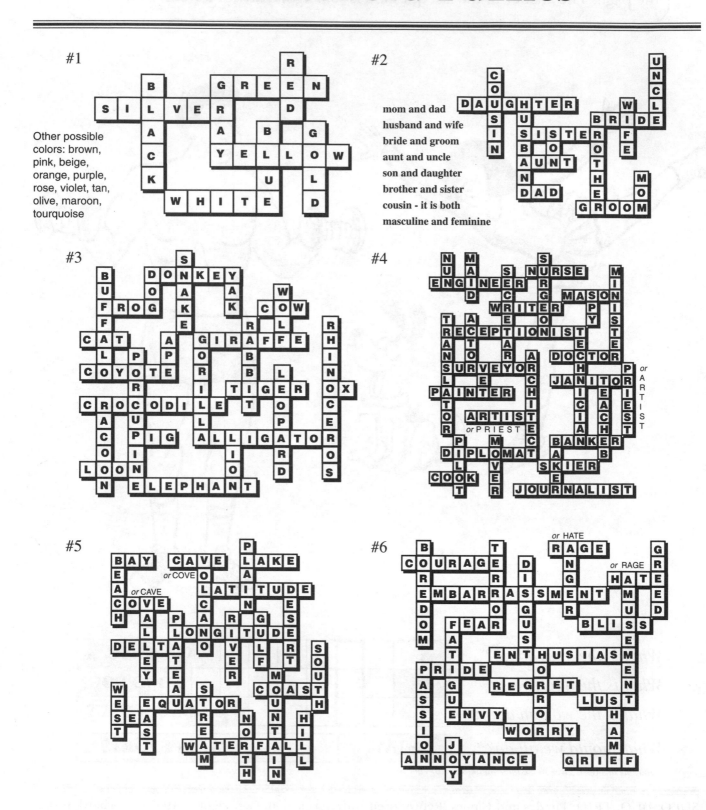

#1

Other possible colors: brown, pink, beige, orange, purple, rose, violet, tan, olive, maroon, tourquoise

#2

mom and dad
husband and wife
bride and groom
aunt and uncle
son and daughter
brother and sister
cousin - it is both masculine and feminine

#3

#4

#5

#6

Answers for the Crossword Puzzles

#7

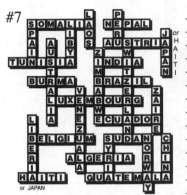

_1_ Algeria	_25_ Libya	
_6_ Australia	_15_ Luxembourg	
_27_ Austria	_12_ Nepal	
_5_ Belgium	_20_ Norway	
_4_ Brazil	_14_ Peru	
_23_ Burma	_17_ Somalia	
_2_ China	_16_ Spain	
_22_ Ecuador	_11_ Sudan	
_9_ Guatemala	_3_ Switzerland	
_21_ Haiti	_8_ Syria	
_19_ India	_26_ Tunisia	
_24_ Japan	_7_ Venezuela	
_28_ Laos	_13_ Zaire	
_18_ Liberia	_10_ Zimbabwe	

#8

1. Thailand / *Thai*
2. Russia / *Russian*
3. Italy / *Italian*
4. Saudi Arabia / *Arabic*
5. Greece / *Greek*
6. Australia / *English*
7. China / *Chinese*
8. Portugal / *Portuguese*
9. Holland / *Dutch*
10. Korea / *Korean*
11. India / *Hindi* or *English*
12. Norway / *Norwegian*
13. France / *French*
14. Ireland / *Irish* or *English*
15. Spain / *Spanish*
16. Czech Republic / *Czech*

#9

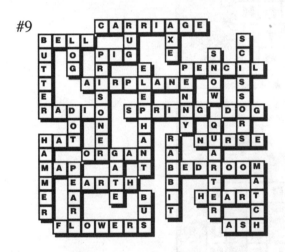

#10

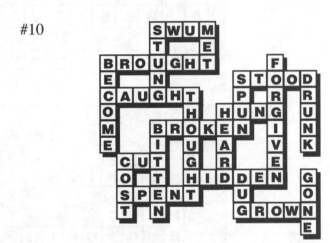

#11

#12

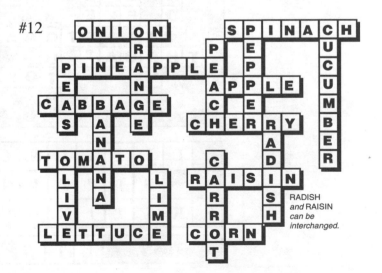

RADISH and RAISIN can be interchanged.

Answers for
the Crossword Puzzles

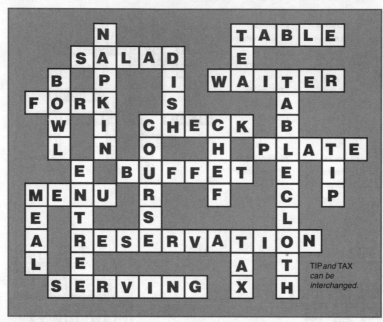

TIP *and* TAX can be interchanged.

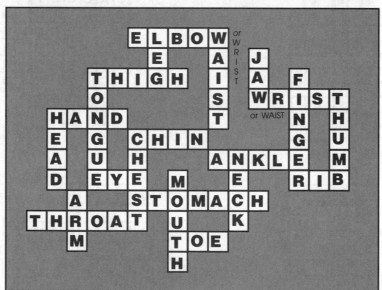

	L	I	F	T	I	N	G	WEIGHTS	
		S	I	T	T	I	N	G	GOOD DOG!
S	K	A	T	I	N	G		SO GRACEFULLY	

STAY		F	I	T	WITH SPORTS

✎ Hidden Wisdom

Instructions

To solve this puzzle, put the white letters at the bottom of each column into the boxes above them in the same column, so that, when you finish, you will be able to read **an English proverb** by reading across the boxes. The gray squares show the ends of words. Some words start on one line and finish on the next. Decide which letter goes into which box by using everything you know about English spelling and grammar. Here is an example:

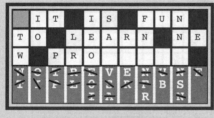

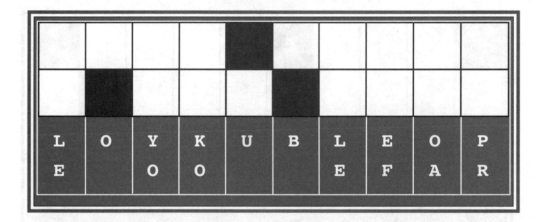

The proverb: __ __ __ __   __ __ __ __ __ __ __

__ __ __ __.

SOLO, DUO, TRIO: Puzzles and Games. Reproduced with permission. Copyright © 1997 by Richard Yorkey
Published by PRO LINGUA ASSOCIATES, 15 Elm Street, Brattleboro, Vermont 05301 USA 800 366 4775

Hidden Wisdom

Instructions

To solve this puzzle, put the white letters at the bottom of each column into the boxes above them in the same column, so that, when you finish, you will be able to read **an English proverb** by reading across the boxes. The gray squares show the ends of words. Some words start on one line and finish on the next. Decide which letter goes into which box by using everything you know about English spelling and grammar. Here is an example:

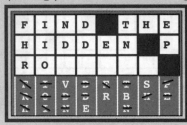

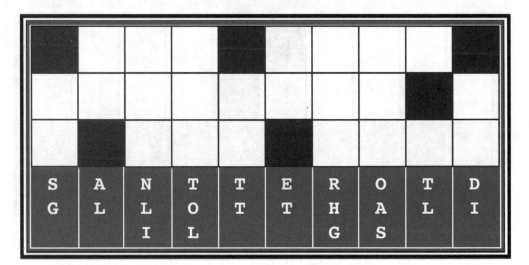

The proverb: ___ ___ ___ ___   ___ ___ ___ ___ ___

___ ___ ___   ___ ___ ___ ___   ___ ___ ___ ___ ___.

Published by PRO LINGUA ASSOCIATES, 15 Elm Street, Brattleboro, Vermont 05301 USA 800 366 4775

To solve this puzzle, put the white letters at the bottom of each column into the boxes above them in the same column, so that, when you finish, you will be able to read **an English proverb** by reading across the boxes. The gray squares show the ends of words. Some words start on one line and finish on the next. Decide which letter goes into which box by using everything you know about English spelling and grammar. Here is an example:

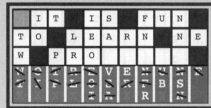

The proverb: __.

SOLO, DUO, TRIO: Puzzles and Games. Reproduced with permission. Copyright © 1997 by Richard Yorkey Published by PRO LINGUA ASSOCIATES, 15 Elm Street, Brattleboro, Vermont 05301 USA 800 366 4775

Hidden Wisdom

To solve this puzzle, put the white letters at the bottom of each column into the boxes above them in the same column, so that, when you finish, you will be able to read **an English proverb** by reading across the boxes. The gray squares show the ends of words. Some words start on one line and finish on the next. Decide which letter goes into which box by using everything you know about English spelling and grammar. Here is an example:

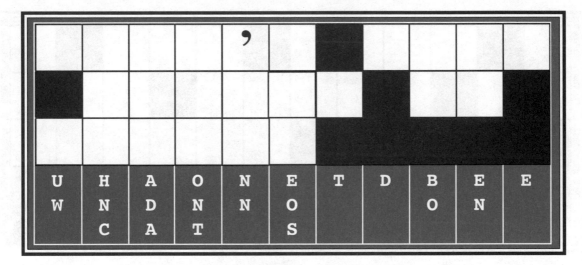

The proverb: __ __ __ __'__ __ __ __ __ __ __ __ __

__ __ __ __ __ __ __ __ __.

SOLO, DUO, TRIO: Puzzles and Games. Reproduced with permission. Copyright © 1997 by Richard Yorkey
Published by PRO LINGUA ASSOCIATES, 15 Elm Street, Brattleboro, Vermont 05301 USA 800 366 4775

Instructions

To solve this puzzle, put the white letters at the bottom of each column into the boxes above them in the same column, so that, when you finish, you will be able to read **an English proverb** by reading across the boxes. The gray squares show the ends of words. Some words start on one line and finish on the next. Decide which letter goes into which box by using everything you know about English spelling and grammar. Here is an example:

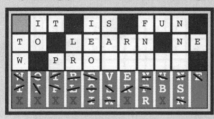

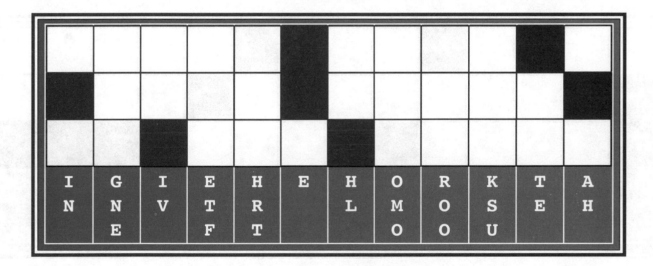

The proverb: __ __ __ __   __ __ __ __ __   __ __   __ __ __ __

__ __ __ __ __ __ __ __ __   __ __ __ __   __ __ __ __ __ __ .

SOLO, DUO, TRIO: Puzzles and Games. Reproduced with permission. Copyright © 1997 by Richard Yorkey
Published by PRO LINGUA ASSOCIATES, 15 Elm Street, Brattleboro, Vermont 05301 USA 800 366 4775

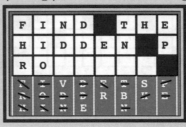

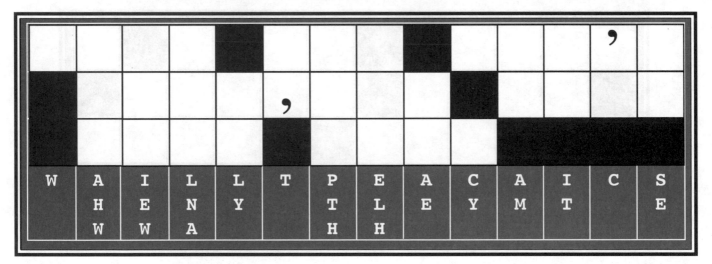

W	A	I	L	L	T	P	E	A	C	A	I	C	S
H	E	N	Y		T	L	Y	E		Y	M	T	E
W	W	A			T	H	H						

The proverb: __ __ __ __ __ __ __   __ __ __   __ __ __ __ __ __ , __ __ __ __ __ __ ,

__ __ __ __   __ __ __ __ __   __ __ __ __ __   __ __ __ __ .

SOLO, DUO, TRIO: Puzzles and Games. Reproduced with permission. Copyright © 1997 by Richard Yorkey
Published by PRO LINGUA ASSOCIATES, 15 Elm Street, Brattleboro, Vermont 05301 USA 800 366 4775

Instructions

To solve this puzzle, put the white letters at the bottom of each column into the boxes above them in the same column, so that, when you finish, you will be able to read **an English proverb** by reading across the boxes. The gray squares show the ends of words. Some words start on one line and finish on the next. Decide which letter goes into which box by using everything you know about English spelling and grammar. Here is an example:

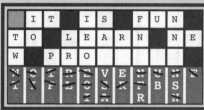

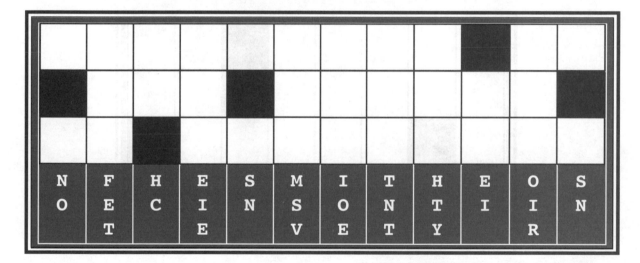

The proverb: __ __ __ __ __ __ __ __ __ __ __ __ __ __

__ __ __ __ __ __ __ __ __ __ __ __ .

SOLO, DUO, TRIO: Puzzles and Games. Reproduced with permission. Copyright © 1997 by Richard Yorkey
Published by PRO LINGUA ASSOCIATES, 15 Elm Street, Brattleboro, Vermont 05301 USA 800 366 4775

✎ Hidden Wisdom

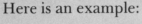

To solve this puzzle, put the white letters at the bottom of each column into the boxes above them in the same column, so that, when you finish, you will be able to read **an English proverb** by reading across the boxes. The gray squares show the ends of words. Some words start on one line and finish on the next. Decide which letter goes into which box by using everything you know about English spelling and grammar. Here is an example:

F	I	N	D		T	H	E
H	I	D	D	E	N		P
R	O						

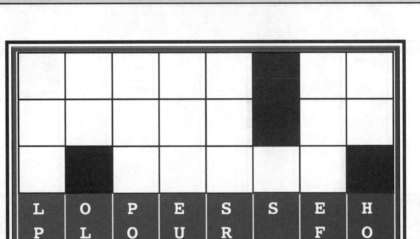

The proverb: __ __ __ __ __ __ __ __ __ __ __ __ __ __

__ __ __ __ __ .

Hidden Wisdom

To solve this puzzle, put the white letters at the bottom of each column into the boxes above them in the same column, so that, when you finish, you will be able to read **an English proverb** by reading across the boxes. The gray squares show the ends of words. Some words start on one line and finish on the next. Decide which letter goes into which box by using everything you know about English spelling and grammar. Here is an example:

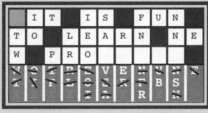

The proverb: __ __ __ __ __ __ __ __ __ __ __ __ __

__ __ __ __ __ __ __ __ __ __ __ .

Answers for the Hidden Wisdom Puzzles

It is fun to learn new proverbs.

Find the hidden proverbs.

#1. Look before you leap.

#2. All that glitters is not gold.

#3. A fool and his money are soon parted.

#4. What's done cannot be undone.

#5. Never look a gift horse in the mouth.

#6. When the cat's away, the mice will play.

#7. Necessity is the mother of invention.

#8. Power follows the purse.

#9. Love laughs at locksmiths.

✏️ A Riddle Puzzle

Instructions

To solve this puzzle, fill in the answers to the clues, putting one letter on each line. Then transfer the letters to the boxes above that have the same numbers. When all the boxes are filled in correctly, you will have the answer to the riddle.

The Riddle

What's the difference between an old ten dollar bill and a new one?

1	2	3	4		5	6	7	8	9	10	11

A. ___ ___ ___ ___ ___
    8 4 9 10 1

(VERB) To find out new information or how to do something. *I hope to _____ more English vocabulary.*

B. ___ ___ ___ ___
    11 6 7 5

(VERB, PAST TENSE) To give something in return for money. *Yesterday I _____ my old car for more than I paid for it!*

C. ___ ___
    2 3

(PREPOSITION) The opposite of **out**. *Please, come ___ and sit down.*

Instructions

To solve this puzzle, fill in the answers to the clues, putting one letter on each line. Then transfer the letters to the boxes above that have the same numbers. When all the boxes are filled in correctly, you will have the answer to the riddle.

The Riddle

What can you have after someone has taken it?

1		2	3	4	5	6	7	8	9	10	11

A. ___ ___ ___ ___
   11 1 8 2

(NOUN) A stringed musical instrument. *I have a friend who expects to be an angel and play a _____ in heaven.*

B. ___ ___ ___ ___
   7 6 9 5

(NOUN) A four-legged animal with horns that gives milk. *That nanny _____ has four little kids.*

C. ___ ___ ___
   3 4 10

(VERB) To jump on one leg. *Johnny hurt his left foot and had to _____ all the way home on his right foot.*

✎ A Riddle Puzzle

Instructions

To solve this puzzle, fill in the answers to the clues, putting one letter on each line. Then transfer the letters to the boxes above that have the same numbers. When all the boxes are filled in correctly, you will have the answer to the riddle.

The Riddle
At what time did God create Adam?

1		2	3	4	5	6	7		8	9	10	11	12	13		14	15	16

A. ___ ___ ___ ___
   15 11 4 14

(VERB) To cast a ballot in an election. *I'm going to _____ for my friend to be our class president.*

B. ___ ___ ___ ___
   8 16 13 10

(NOUN) The meat from farm cattle. *We always eat roast _____ for Sunday dinner.*

C. ___ ___ ___ ___
   12 7 1 6

(ADJECTIVE) Actual; true, not made up or imaginary. *Honest! The UFO I saw was _____!*

D. ___ ___ ___ ___
   5 3 2 9

(NOUN) A flat piece of baked clay used on walls and floors. *I accidentally broke a _____ on our bathroom floor.*

SOLO, DUO, TRIO: Puzzles and Games. Reproduced with permission. Copyright © 1997 by Richard Yorkey Published by PRO LINGUA ASSOCIATES, 15 Elm Street, Brattleboro, Vermont 05301 USA 800 366 4775

A Riddle Puzzle

Instructions

To solve this puzzle, fill in the answers to the clues, putting one letter on each line. Then transfer the letters to the boxes above that have the same numbers. When all the boxes are filled in correctly, you will have the answer to the riddle.

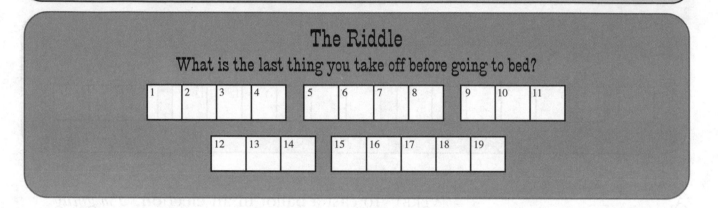

The Riddle
What is the last thing you take off before going to bed?

| 1 | 2 | 3 | 4 | | 5 | 6 | 7 | 8 | | 9 | 10 | 11 |

| 12 | 13 | 14 | | 15 | 16 | 17 | 18 | 19 |

A. ___ ___ ___
    9 15 5

(PREPOSITION) Opposite of **on**. *Take _____ your clothes and put on your pajamas.*

B. ___ ___ ___ ___ ___
    1 17 3 8 13

(NOUN) Early life; the period of being young; a young person. *Her _____ is admired by older men and women.*

C. ___ ___ ___ ___ ___
   10 16 6 14 12

(NOUN) A large number of ships. *A _____ of ships sailed into New York harbor.*

D. ___ ___ ___ ___ ___ ___
    4 18 2 11 7 19

(NOUN) A person who puts roofs on buildings. *The _____ fell off the roof and broke his back.*

SOLO, DUO, TRIO: Puzzles and Games. Reproduced with permission. Copyright © 1997 by Richard Yorkey
Published by PRO LINGUA ASSOCIATES, 15 Elm Street, Brattleboro, Vermont 05301 USA 800 366 4775

A Riddle Puzzle

#5

Instructions

To solve this puzzle, fill in the answers to the clues, putting one letter on each line. Then transfer the letters to the boxes above that have the same numbers. When all the boxes are filled in correctly, you will have the answer to the riddle.

The Riddle
Who invented the first airplane that didn't fly?

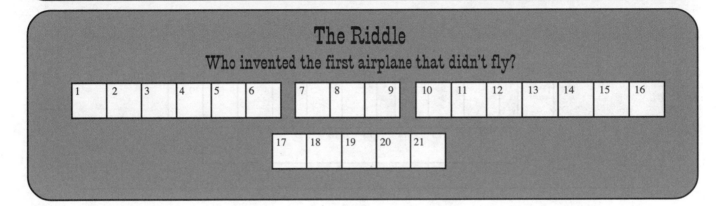

| 1 | 2 | 3 | 4 | 5 | 6 | | 7 | 8 | 9 | | 10 | 11 | 12 | 13 | 14 | 15 | 16 |

| 17 | 18 | 19 | 20 | 21 |

A. ___ ___ ___ ___
   16 12 2 14

(ADJECTIVE) Sinful, wicked. *she says very bad things about people; she has an _____ tongue.*

B. ___ ___ ___ ___
   4 3 10 1

(VERB) To send out a strong current of air. *Close the window or else the wind will _____ out the candles.*

C. ___ ___ ___ ___
   15 7 11 9

(NOUN) Fat from pigs, used in cooking. *I use butter rather than _____ when I bake cookies.*

D. ___ ___ ___ ___
   6 5 13 8

(VERB) To spoil or cause serious damage. *If this rain continues, it will really _____ our vacation.*

E. ___ ___ ___ ___ ___
   21 18 19 17 20

(VERB, PAST PARTICIPLE) To increase in size by natural development. *My son has _____ two inches already this year.*

SOLO, DUO, TRIO: Puzzles and Games. Reproduced with permission. Copyright © 1997 by Richard Yorkey Published by PRO LINGUA ASSOCIATES, 15 Elm Street, Brattleboro, Vermont 05301 USA 800 366 4775

A Riddle Puzzle

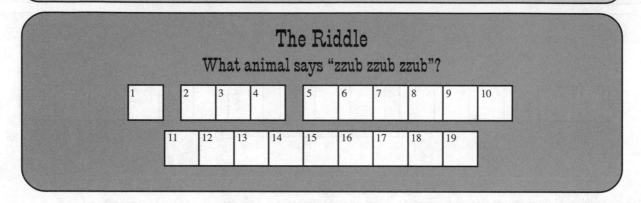

Instructions

To solve this puzzle, fill in the answers to the clues, putting one letter on each line. Then transfer the letters to the boxes above that have the same numbers. When all the boxes are filled in correctly, you will have the answer to the riddle.

The Riddle
What animal says "zzub zzub zzub"?

| 1 | | 2 | 3 | 4 | | 5 | 6 | 7 | 8 | 9 | 10 |

| 11 | 12 | 13 | 14 | 15 | 16 | 17 | 18 | 19 |

A. ___ ___ ___ ___ ___
    5 1 11 6 3

(NOUN) A short story, usually about animals, that teaches a lesson. *"The Fox and the Grapes" is a _____ by Aesop..*

B. ___ ___ ___ ___
   2 17 16 10

(VERB) To boast; to say many good things. *She likes to _____ about her intelligence and beauty.*

C. ___ ___ ___ ___
  19 14 8 18

(VERB) To slide sideways, as a car sometimes does on wet or ice roads. *Because of the snow, the car started to _____ out of control.*

D. ___ ___ ___
  13 12 9

(NOUN) A small, closed metal container in which food and drinks are preserved without air. *We can open a _____ of tune fish and make a salad or sandwiches.*

E. ___ ___ ___
  7 4 15

(NOUN) A tree with small dark green leaves and red berries. *In poetry, the _____ tree is a symbol of sadness or death.*

✎ A Riddle Puzzle

Instructions

To solve this puzzle, fill in the answers to the clues, putting one letter on each line. Then transfer the letters to the boxes above that have the same numbers. When all the boxes are filled in correctly, you will have the answer to the riddle.

The Riddle
What says "ouch, ouch, ouch, ouch, ouch, ouch, ouch, ouch" when it walks?

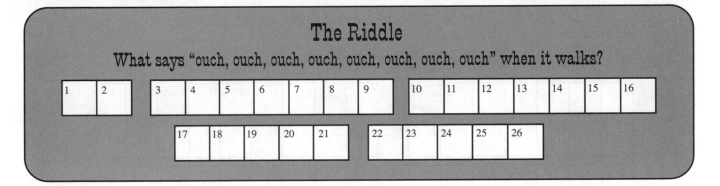

A. ___ ___ ___ ___ ___
   17 24 7 14 4

(NOUN) A subject or theme. *Write a conposition on the _____ of "What I Did Last Summer."*

B. ___ ___ ___ ___ ___
   22 10 6 13 11

(VERB, PAST TENSE) To curse; use bad language. *I _____ when I accidentally hit my finger with the hammer.*

C. ___ ___ ___ ___ ___
   21 23 18 15 19

(NOUN) Any object that is not named. *What do you use this _____ for?*

D. ___ ___ ___ ___ ___
   20 3 8 26 25

(NOUN) A building for people to live in. *We had to sell our _____ when we moved to another city.*

E. ___ ___ ___
   16 1 9

(NOUN) A petroleum product that powers automobiles and airplanes. *If we don't stop at the next station, we may run out of _____.*

F. ___ ___ ___
   12 2 5

(NOUN) A small insect; a pest at picnics. *An _____ was crawling on her sandwich.*

SOLO, DUO, TRIO: Puzzles and Games. Reproduced with permission. Copyright © 1997 by Richard Yorkey Published by PRO LINGUA ASSOCIATES, 15 Elm Street, Brattleboro, Vermont 05301 USA 800 366 4775

✏️ A Riddle Puzzle

The Riddle
What is the longest word in the dictionary?

1	2	3	4	5	6		7	8	9	10	11		12	13

14	15	16	17	18	19	20		21	22	23		24	25	26	27	28

29	30	31		32	33	34	35		36	37	38	39	40	41	42

A. _____ _____ _____ _____
   40 7 28 34

(VERB, 3PS) To chew or swallow food. *Betty _____ three nutritious meals a day.*

B. _____ _____ _____ _____
   42 10 19 17

(VERB, PAST TENSE) To kill violently. *The knight _____ the dragon and rescued the maiden.*

C. _____ _____ _____ _____ _____
   14 4 37 11 31

(VERB) To lose blood. *Unless we put a tourniquet on his arm, this boy will _____ to death.*

D. _____ _____ _____ _____ _____ _____
   24 29 13 39 15 41

(ADJ., COMPARATIVE) Rapid; moving a great speed. *The Concorde can fly _____ than any other commercial airplain.*

E. _____ _____ _____ _____ _____ _____
   6 25 8 26 32 21

(NOUN) An expression that compares one thing to another, using the words **like** or **as**. *"As quiet as a mouse" is a _____.*

F. _____ _____ _____ _____ _____ _____
   38 22 9 26 27 21

(NOUN) Desire or need for a drink. *After a week without water in the desert, the soldiers died of _____.*

G. _____ _____ _____ _____ _____ _____ _____ _____ _____ _____ _____
   1 18 30 16 3 2 5 20 35 33 36

(ADJ.) Showing tender feelings rather than reasonable or practical judgments. *My old car doesn't work very well anymore, but it still has a _____ value for me.*

✎ A Riddle Puzzle

Instructions

To solve this puzzle, fill in the answers to the clues, putting one letter on each line. Then transfer the letters to the boxes above that have the same numbers. When all the boxes are filled in correctly, you will have the answer to the riddle.

The Riddle
Why didn't the skeleton have a good time at the dance?

| 1 | 2 | 3 | 4 | 5 | 6 | 7 | | 8 | 9 | 10 | | 11 | 12 | 13 | | 14 | 15 |

| 16 | 17 | 18 | 19 | | 20 | 21 | | 22 | 23 | 24 | 25 | 26 | | 27 | 28 | 29 | 30 |

A. ___ ___ ___ ___ ___
  29 7 24 8 26

(NOUN) A verb form that shows the time of the action. *Many students are not sure of the difference between the simple past and the present perfect _____.*

B. ___ ___ ___ ___ ___
  27 11 28 3 9

(PRONOUN) A word used in questions that introduce a choice. *Mary's not sure _____ umbrella to buy, this black one or that polka dot one.*

C. ___ ___ ___ ___ ___ ___
  16 5 13 22 30 4

(PROPER NOUN) A religious philosopher and teacher who lived in India in the 5th century BC. *Siddartha Gautama is know as _____ and embodies wisdom and virtue.*

D. ___ ___ ___ ___
  1 21 15 20

(NOUN) A covering of leather or rubber for the foot and ankle, usually heavier than a shoe. *William lost a _____ in the woods and had to continue his hike with one bare foot!*

E. ___ ___ ___ ___
  14 17 6 10

(NOUN) The part of the face used for smelling. *"The skunk smell was so bad that I had to hold my _____.*

F. ___ ___ ___
  23 25 2

(NOUN) A playing card that has a single spot, either the highest or the lowest card. *In bridge, the top cards are jack, queen, king, and _____.*

G. ___ ___ ___
  18 12 19

(NOUN) A period of 24 hours. *Our vacation begins the _____ after tomorrow.*

SOLO, DUO, TRIO: Puzzles and Games. Reproduced with permission. Copyright © 1997 by Richard Yorkey Published by PRO LINGUA ASSOCIATES, 15 Elm Street, Brattleboro, Vermont 05301 USA 800 366 4775

# A Riddle Puzzle

---

Instructions

To solve this puzzle, fill in the answers to the clues, putting one letter on each line. Then transfer the letters to the boxes above that have the same numbers. When all the boxes are filled in correctly, you will have the answer to the riddle.

The Riddle
Why do all birds fly south in the winter?

| 1 | 2 | 3 | 4 | | 5 | 6 | 7 | , | 8 | | 9 | 10 | 11 | 12 | 13 | 14 |

| 15 | 16 | | 17 | 18 | 19 | 20 | | 21 | 22 | 23 | | 24 | 25 | 26 | 27 | 28 |

A. ___ ___ ___
  4 23 17

(ADVERB) By a particular time; already. *Has Mary Gomez arrived _____?*

B. ___ ___ ___
  10 26 15

(ADJECTIVE) Big and round; thick and well-filled. *Too much icecream and cake causes people to get _____.*

C. ___ ___ ___ ___
  8 13 27 12

(NOUN) A group of three people. *The Kingston _____ was the most popular singing group of the 1950's and 60's..*

D. ___ ___ ___ ___
  2 20 6 21

(NOUN) Warmth; hotness. *We dried our wet clothes by the _____ of the fire.*

E. ___ ___ ___ ___
  5 22 18 1

(NOUN) A friendly, informal conversation. *My friend and I like to _____ about the old days in high school.*

F. ___ ___ ___ ___ ___
  11 25 16 7 24

(NOUN) The most forward position, farthest from or opposite to the back. *The teacher asked the little girl to come to the _____ of the classroom.*

G. ___ ___ ___ ___ ___
  28 9 19 3 14

(ADJ.) Nude, not covered by clothes. *The man had taken off his shirt and was _____ to the waist.*

✏️ A Riddle Puzzle

The Riddle
In what month do people talk the least?

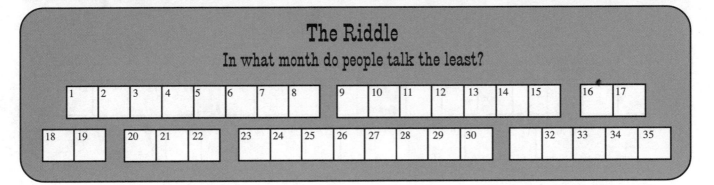

A. ___ ___
  25 33

(PREPOSITION) Opposite of **off**. *Henry put his engagement ring _____ her finger.*

B. ___ ___ ___
  9   5   20

(CONJUNCTION) Against what might be expected; however. *It was cold and rainy _____ we went on a picnic anyway.*

C. ___ ___ ___
  26 6   8

(NOUN) A narrow beam of light. *His daughter's visit brought a _____ of sunshine into the old man's life.*

D. ___ ___ ___ ___
  1   12 11 15

(NOUN) The front part of the head, from the forehead to the chin. *She had a surprised expression on her _____.*

E. ___ ___ ___ ___
  3   10 2   4

(NOUN) An alcoholic drink made of malt and hops. *Would you like a bottle of _____ or a glass of wine?*

F. ___ ___ ___ ___
  29 24 13 17

(VERB) To close. *We had to _____ the door to keep out the loud noise.*

G. ___ ___ ___ ___ ___
  30 35 22 14 28

(DEMONSTRATIVE PRONOUN, PLURAL) *I think I'll buy _____ socks instead of those.*

H. ___ ___ ___ ___ ___
  31 32 18 23 34

(ADJECTIVE) Slightly wet; damp. *The unhappy woman's eyes were _____ with tears.*

I. ___ ___ ___ ___ ___
  19 21 16 7   27

(NOUN) A man's clothing for the upper part of his body. *John has to wear a _____ and tie in his office.*

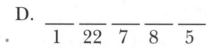 A Riddle Puzzle

Instructions

To solve this puzzle, fill in the answers to the clues, putting one letter on each line. Then transfer the letters to the boxes above that have the same numbers. When all the boxes are filled in correctly, you will have the answer to the riddle.

The Riddle

Which burns longer, the candles on a girl's birthday cake or the candles on a boy's birthday cake?

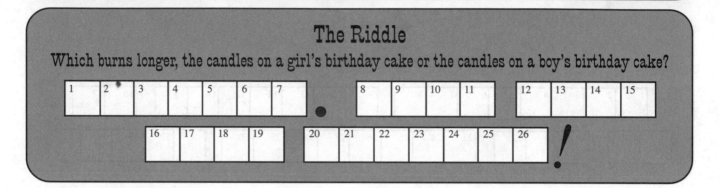

| 1 | 2 | 3 | 4 | 5 | 6 | 7 | | 8 | 9 | 10 | 11 | | 12 | 13 | 14 | 15 |

| 16 | 17 | 18 | 19 | | 20 | 21 | 22 | 23 | 24 | 25 | 26 |

A. ___ ___ ___
   21 2 11

(EXCLAMTION) A word you use to get someone's attention. "_____! *Where are you going?*"

B. ___ ___ ___
   18 13 24

(VERB) To go bad; to decay. *When apples fall off a tree, they often _____ on the ground.*

C. ___ ___ ___ ___
   4 15 3 19

(ADJECTIVE) Not wide or fat; opposite of **thick**. *After my father lost so much weight, he looked very _____.*

D. ___ ___ ___ ___ ___
   1 22 7 8 5

(NOUN) A compass direction, opposite of **south**. *Canada is _____ of the United States, which is _____ of Mexico.*

E. ___ ___ ___ ___ ___
   14 9 25 20 10

(PRONOUN) The plural form of **this**. *Which of _____ sweaters do you like best.*

F. ___ ___ ___ ___ ___ ___
   26 17 12 16 6 23

(NOUN) A material that springs back into position when it is stretched. *Automobile tires are made of _____.*

✎ A Riddle Puzzle

Instructions

To solve this puzzle, fill in the answers to the clues, putting one letter on each line. Then transfer the letters to the boxes above that have the same numbers. When all the boxes are filled in correctly, you will have the answer to the riddle.

The Riddle

What are two things you can never have for breakfast?

1	2	3	4	5		6	7	8		9	10	11	12	13	14

A. ___ ___ ___
    12 2 7

(NOUN) A woman who belongs to a religious group. *Sister Agatha is a _____ in the Notre Dame Convent.*

B. ___ ___ ___
   6 11 9

(CONJUNCTION) Plus; in addition to. *There are many men _____ women in our class.*

C. ___ ___ ___ ___ ___ ___ ___ ___
   4 5 10 1 8 14 13 3

(PLURAL NOUN) *Janet and John Martin have three _____, two girls and one boy.*

✏️ A Riddle Puzzle

Instructions

To solve this puzzle, fill in the answers to the clues, putting one letter on each line. Then transfer the letters to the boxes above that have the same numbers. When all the boxes are filled in correctly, you will have the answer to the riddle.

The Riddle
What is a twack?

1	2	3	4	5	6	7	8	9		10

11	12	13	14	15		16	17	18	19		20	21

A. ___ ___
  8 20

(ADVERB) The opposite of **yes**. "_____, I don't want to go to the movies tonight"

B. ___ ___ ___
  10 14 3

(NOUN) The act of pointing a gun at some object. The hunter took careful _____ before he shot the deer.

C. ___ ___ ___
  12 7 18

(VERB) To be the best or first in a battle, race, or game. "We can't lose this game. We have to _____!"

D. ___ ___ ___ ___
  19 2 21 9

(NOUN) A short piece of music with words for singing. "Let's sing the happy birthday _____ for Mary!"

E. ___ ___ ___ ___
  5 17 16 15

(VERB) To move yourself or an object to the left or right or all the way around. Paul had to _____ the wheels of his car quickly to avoid hitting a tree.

F. ___ ___ ___ ___ ___
  6 13 1 11 4

(NOUN) Quick movement, hurry; speed. Sue packed her suitcase in _____ because she was late for the plane.

SOLO, DUO, TRIO: Puzzles and Games. Reproduced with permission. Copyright © 1997 by Richard Yorkey Published by PRO LINGUA ASSOCIATES, 15 Elm Street, Brattleboro, Vermont 05301 USA 800 366 4775

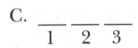

A Riddle Puzzle

Instructions

To solve this puzzle, fill in the answers to the clues, putting one letter on each line. Then transfer the letters to the boxes above that have the same numbers. When all the boxes are filled in correctly, you will have the answer to the riddle.

The Riddle

What belongs to you but is used more often by others?

1	2	3	4		5	6	7	8

A. ___ ___
   7   8

(PRONOUN) The object form of the first person singual, **I**. *"Please give it to _____."*

B. ___ ___ ___
   4   6   5

(VERB, PAST TENSE) Moved quickly with your feet. *Henry was late, so he _____ all the way to school.*

C. ___ ___ ___
   1   2   3

(PRONOUN) The person being talked to; second person singular. *"How are _____? _____ look very happy today."*

SOLO, DUO, TRIO: Puzzles and Games. Reproduced with permission. Copyright © 1997 by Richard Yorkey
Published by PRO LINGUA ASSOCIATES, 15 Elm Street, Brattleboro, Vermont 05301 USA 800 366 4775

✏️ A Riddle Puzzle

Instructions

To solve this puzzle, fill in the answers to the clues, putting one letter on each line. Then transfer the letters to the boxes above that have the same numbers. When all the boxes are filled in correctly, you will have the answer to the riddle.

The Riddle

What is worse than finding a worm in your apple?

1	2	3	4	5	6	7		8	9	10	11

12		13	14	15	16

A. ___ ___ ___
   12 3 4

(CONJUNCTION) In addition to; plus. *I like to eat bacon _____ eggs for breakfast.*

B. ___ ___ ___ ___
   13 8 14 16

(PRONOUN) The object form of the relative pronoun, **who**. *She is a person _____ I don't like very much.*

C. ___ ___ ___ ___
   1 9 5 15

(ADJECTIVE) Quite good; not bad, but not excellent either. *His spoken English is good but his writing is only _____.*

D. ___ ___ ___ ___ ___
   11 10 2 6 7

(VERB) To throw something with great force. *My dog catches the frisbee every time I _____ it to him.*

✎ A Riddle Puzzle

Instructions

To solve this puzzle, fill in the answers to the clues, putting one letter on each line. Then transfer the letters to the boxes above that have the same numbers. When all the boxes are filled in correctly, you will have the answer to the riddle.

The Riddle
What is the difference between a jeweler and a jailer?

1	2	3		4	5	6	7	8		9	10	11	12	13	14	15

16	17	18		19	20	21		22	23	24	25	26

27	28	29	30	31	32	33		34	35	36	37	38

A. ___ ___ ___
   17 32 11

(ADJECTIVE) The money remaining after all expenses are paid. *The _____ profit of Margaret's business was small.*

B. ___ ___ ___ ___
   26 1   6   37

(VERB) To move along by turning over and over. *This desk is not level so your pencils may _____ off the edge.*

C. ___ ___ ___ ___
   12 31 22 9

(NOUN) A slang word for food, especially hearty dishes or a meal. *Soldiers are never happy about the _____ they are served in the army.*

D. ___ ___ ___ ___ ___
   30 20 16 8   3

(VERB) To run after someone or something. *The police officer had to _____ the thief for four blocks before she caught him.*

E. ___ ___ ___ ___ ___
   18 5   10 23 13

(NOUN) The end of life. *After the soldier's _____, his body was sent home to be buried.*

F. ___ ___ ___ ___ ___
   2   14 38 19 33

(PLURAL NOUN) Homes built by birds where they lay their eggs and raise their young. *Different kids of birds have built several _____ in the tree beside my house.*

G. ___ ___ ___ ___ ___ ___
   34 28 4   29 36 21

(NOUN) A large building, or group of buildings, with stone walls to defend against attack. *King Richard and his knights once visited this famous _____ in Syria.*

H. ___ ___ ___ ___ ___ ___
   27 24 25 35 7   15

(plural noun) A circular frame which turns on a central point or axle. *By difinition, a bicycle has two _____.*

SOLO, DUO, TRIO: Puzzles and Games. Reproduced with permission. Copyright © 1997 by Richard Yorkey
Published by PRO LINGUA ASSOCIATES, 15 Elm Street, Brattleboro, Vermont 05301 USA 800 366 4775

Answers for the Riddle Puzzles

#1 nine dollars
A. learn
B. sold
C. in

#2 a photograph
A. harp
B. goat
C. hop

#3 a little before Eve
A. vote
B. beef
C. real
D. tile

4# your feet off the floor
A. off
B. youth
C. fleet
D. roofer

#5 Wilber and Orville Wrong
A. evil
B. blow
C. lard
D. ruin
E. grown

6# a bee flying backwards
A. fable
B. brag
C. skid
D. can
E. yew

7# an octopus wearing tight shoes
A. topic
B. swore
C. thing
D. house
E. gas
F. ant

#8 Smiles. There is a mile between the first and last letters.
A. eats
B. slew
C. bleed
D. faster
E. simile
F. thirst
G. sentimental

#9 because she had no body to dance with.
A. tense
B. which
C. Buddha
D. boot
E. nose
F. ace
G. day

#10 They can't afford to take the train.
A. yet
B. fat
C. trio
D. heat
E. chat
F. front
G. naked

#11 February, because it is the shortest month.
A. on
B. but
C. ray
D. face
E. beer
F. shut
G. these
H. moist
I. shirt

#12 Neither. They both burn shorter.
A. hey
B. rot
C. thin
D. north
E. these
F. rubber

#13 lunch and dinner
A. nun
B. and
C. children

#14 something a twain runs on
A. no
B. aim
C. win
D. song
E. turn
F. haste

#15 your name
A. me
B. ran
C. you

#16 finding half a worm
A. and
B. whom
C. fair
D. fling

#17 One sells watches and the other watches cells.
A. net
B. roll
C. chow
D. chase
E. death
F. nests
G. castle
H. wheels

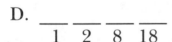 # A Double-Crostic Puzzle #1

Instructions

To solve this puzzle, fill in the answers to the clues, putting one letter on each numbered line. Then transfer the letters to the boxes below that have the same numbers. When all the boxes are filled in correctly, you will be able to read a common proverb in English.

The Clues

A. __ __ __ __ __
   6 16 9 12 14

n. The manner in which something is done, typical of a person, a group, or time of history. *His painting is done in the modern _____ of Picasso.*

B. __ __ __ __ __
  21 17 11 19 10

adj. Not thin. *That large dictionary is too _____ to fit in the space between the books on the bookshelf.*

C. __ __ __ __
  3 5 20 15

n. A thoroughfare or street. *There are too many cars on this _____. It's a real traffic jam!*

D. __ __ __ __
  1 2 8 18

adj. Attractive in an interesting or amusing way. *Oh, your baby is so _____!*

E. __ __ __
  13 4 7

The number 52 in Roman numerals.
Claudius was emperor of Rome in the year _____ A.D.

The Proverb

1	2	3	4	5	6	7	8	9		10	11	12	13	14	15

16	17	18		19	20	21

Note: This is a variation of the double-crostic form.

SOLO, DUO, TRIO: Puzzles and Games. Reproduced with permission. Copyright © 1997 by Richard Yorkey
Published by PRO LINGUA ASSOCIATES, 15 Elm Street, Brattleboro, Vermont 05301 USA 800 366 4775

✎ A Double-Crostic Puzzle #2

The Clues

A. __ __ __ __ __ __ __ __
 3 17 8 29 12 20 7 22

n. One of two periods into which a college year is divided. *She passed her English course during the first _____ of her freshman year.*

B. __ __ __ __ __ __
 6 16 1 5 21 11

n. Money that is returned to you after you pay more than the cost of what you're buying. *The groceries cost $19.23 so I won't get very much _____ from my 20-dollar bill.*

C. __ __ __ __ __
 14 4 9 30 28

v. Past tense of **hear**. STUDENT: *The dog ate my homework.* TEACHER: *That's the silliest excuse I've ever _____!*

D. __ __ __ __
 25 26 19 10

n. A utensil for holding and carrying food to your mouth which has a handle on one end and 3 or 4 points on the other. *Each place setting has a knife, a _____, and a spoon.*

E. __ __ __ __
 13 23 24 27

n. An area with houses and other buildings where people live and work, smaller than a city but larger than a village. *I 'd rather live in a small _____ than a large city.*

F. __ __ __
 18 2 15

proper noun. Abraham Lincoln was known as Honest _____.

The Proverb

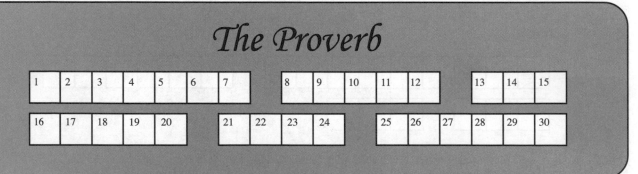

1	2	3	4	5	6	7		8	9	10	11	12		13	14	15
16	17	18	19	20		21	22	23	24		25	26	27	28	29	30

✎ A Double-Crostic Puzzle #3

The Clues

A. ___ ___ ___ ___ ___ ___ ___
   12 19 26 10 17 28 14

n. One who goes and spends time in a place or with someone. *Yesterday an unwelcome _____ came to my door – a bill collector!*

B. ___ ___ ___ ___ ___
   9 2 4 29 20

v. To use the correct letters in the correct order to form a word. *I can never remember how to _____ the word* **occurrence.**

C. ___ ___ ___ ___ ___
   8 25 22 23 31

prep. From some time in the past up to the present. *Henry has been studying English _____ 1995.*

D. ___ ___ ___ ___ ___
   5 6 7 11 30

n. A human being who is older than a baby but younger than an adolescent. *When Lucy was only a _____, she was afraid of thunder and lightning.*

E. ___ ___ ___ ___
   18 13 24 32

v. Past participle of **see**. *I can't find my car keys. Have you _____ them?*

F. ___ ___ ___
   16 1 21

v. To do something with something made for a special purpose. *If you don't know the meaning of a word, _____ your dictionary.*

G. ___ ___ ___
   15 3 27

v. To ask (especially for food or money) in a way which shows little pride or self-respect. *In some cities, many poor people ____ for money.*

The Proverb

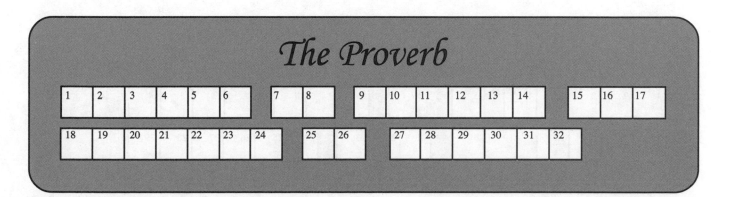

SOLO, DUO, TRIO: Puzzles and Games. Reproduced with permission. Copyright © 1997 by Richard Yorkey
Published by **PRO LINGUA ASSOCIATES**, 15 Elm Street, Brattleboro, Vermont 05301 USA 800 366 4775

A Double-Crostic Puzzle #4

#4

Instructions

To solve this puzzle, fill in the answers to the clues, putting one letter on each numbered line. Then transfer the letters to the boxes below that have the same numbers. When all the boxes are filled in correctly, you will be able to read a common proverb in English.

The Clues

A. __ __ __ __ __ __ __
   9 25 14 16 23 26 7

adj. The biggest. *Alaska is the _____ state in the United States.*

B. __ __ __ __ __
  18 2 13 22 1

n. Anything which can be heard. *Willie is afraid of the _____ of thunder.*

C. __ __ __ __
  5 8 17 28

n. One side of a sheet of paper in a book, magazine, or newspaper. *The footnote is printed at the foot, or bottom, of the _____.*

D. __ __ __ __
 10 19 27 15

v. To be fond of or pleased with someone or something. *Everyone seems to _____ ice cream.*

E. __ __ __
 24 6 11

v. To purchase. *How many 32-cent stamps can I _____ with a dollar?*

F. __ __ __
 4 21 20

n. A measurement of weight; 2000 pounds. *His truck can carry about a _____ of bricks.*

G. __ __ __
 3 12 29

adv. A word used to change a verb, adjective, or another adverb to the opposite meaning. *I liked the movie, but my friend did _____ like it at all .*

The Proverb

1	2	3	'	4		5	6	7		8	9	10		11	12	13	14

15	16	17	18		19	20		21	22	23		24	25	26	27	28	29

SOLO, DUO, TRIO: Puzzles and Games. Reproduced with permission. Copyright © 1997 by Richard Yorkey
Published by PRO LINGUA ASSOCIATES, 15 Elm Street, Brattleboro, Vermont 05301 USA 800 366 4775

A Double-Crostic Puzzle

To solve this puzzle, fill in the answers to the clues, putting one letter on each numbered line. Then transfer the letters to the boxes below that have the same numbers. When all the boxes are filled in correctly, you will be able to read a common proverb in English.

The Clues

A. _____ _____ _____
   29 19 26

Third person singular pronoun. *My wife wore _____ very best dress to church.*

B. _____ _____ _____
   22 7 10

v. To pay money; to purchase. *Henry didn't have enough money to _____ the car he wanted.*

C. _____ _____ _____
   28 36 27

definite article. *"Aladdin" is _____ best Disney movie I've ever seen.*

D. _____ _____ _____
   34 6 31

n. Something to play with. *Barbie Doll is my daughter's favorite _____.*

E. _____ _____ _____ _____
   20 2 11 3

n. 12:00 midday. *The sun is right above your head at _____.*

F. _____ _____ _____ _____
   1 25 35 18

n. A structure in the water, to dive from or where boats tie up. *At our cottage on the lake, we built a wooden _____ out into the water..*

G. _____ _____ _____ _____ _____
   4 13 12 21 9

n. Belief; the faith that something or someone is good and true. *On American money is written the motto, "In God we _____."*

H. _____ _____ _____ _____ _____
   17 32 16 30 24

n. or adj. A leader or the most important person or thing. *The _____ export of Saudi Arabia is oil.*

I. _____ _____ _____ _____ _____ _____
   5 15 33 8 14 23

n. An opportunity: luck. *My brother has failed his driving test twice; next week will be his last _____ to pass it.*

The Proverb

1	2	3	,	4		5	6	7	8	9		10	11	12	13

14	15	16	17	18	19	20	21		22	23	24	25	26	27

28	29	30	31		32	33	34	35	36

SOLO, DUO, TRIO: Puzzles and Games. Reproduced with permission. Copyright © 1997 by Richard Yorkey
Published by PRO LINGUA ASSOCIATES, 15 Elm Street, Brattleboro, Vermont 05301 USA 800 366 4775

The Clues

A. ___ ___ ___
   2 14 22

n. Thick, cloudy air, difficult to see through. *Sometimes the _____ is so thick that you can't see across the street.*

B. ___ ___ ___
  18 12 26

v. To join cloth together with a needle and thread. *Bernice likes to _____ her own clothes.*

C. ___ ___ ___
  19 23 30

adj. Not good. *Sammy is a naughty boy. No one wants to play with him because he is so _____.*

D. ___ ___ ___ ___
  3 32 8 17

adj. Understanding a lot of things; to have good sense and judgment. *Everyone loved King Solomon because he was such a _____ ruler.*

E. ___ ___ ___ ___ ___
  28 16 7 11 25

n. Those who make use of something. *Students who are regular _____ of a dictionary generally have a better vocabulary than those who don't.*

F. ___ ___ ___ ___ ___
  10 24 31 27 15

n. A mistake. *The composition teacher took off one point for each _____ in grammar.*

G. ___ ___ ___ ___ ___
  9 34 1 21 6

v. To find out how heavy something is, using scales. *Men tend to be larger and _____ more than women.*

H. ___ ___ ___ ___ ___ ___
  5 13 4 20 29 33

n. Something that you hide behind, or hold up to protect yourself from attack. *The Roman soldier used his sword and _____ to defend himself.*

The Proverb

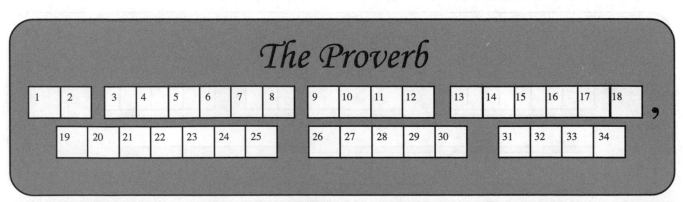

1	2		3	4	5	6	7	8		9	10	11	12		13	14	15	16	17	18

,

19	20	21	22	23	24	25		26	27	28	29	30		31	32	33	34

✏️ A Double-Crostic Puzzle #7

#7

Instructions

To solve this puzzle, fill in the answers to the clues, putting one letter on each numbered line. Then transfer the letters to the boxes below that have the same numbers. When all the boxes are filled in correctly, you will be able to read a proverb that used to be popular in Vermont. Though it is not heard so often now, it is still true.

The Clues

A. __ __ __ __
   14 2 5 18

proper noun. The name of one of the earliest universities in the United States, located in New Haven, Connecticut. *The Latin motto of _____ University is* Lux et Veritas, *which means Light and Truth.*

B. __ __ __ __
   7 13 10 4

past tense v. To go down; to drop below the surface of the water. *There was such a big hole in the bottom of our rowboat that the boat _____ within a few minutes.*

C. __ __ __ __ __
   3 6 9 12 1

adv. A superlative; the antonym of **most**. *Goa is one of the smallest and _____ powerful countries in Africa.*

D. __ __ __ __ __
   11 16 17 15 8

n. pl. A shortened form of the word that describes buildings in a university where students sleep and study, usually two to a room. *During exam time, in the _____ you can see lights on until morning.*

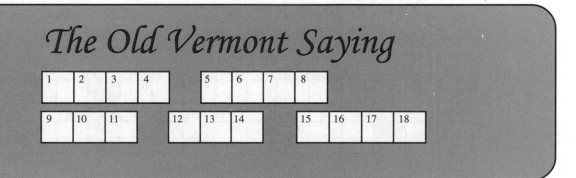

The Old Vermont Saying

1	2	3	4		5	6	7	8

9	10	11		12	13	14		15	16	17	18

✐ A Double-Crostic Puzzle #8

The Clues

A. ___ ___ ___ ___ ___
   23 1 22 11 7

n. A woman who has magic powers to make bad things happen to people. *In the Land of Oz Dorothy met the Wicked _____ of the West.*

B. ___ ___ ___ ___ ___
   2 26 21 9 20

n. An enjoyable, carefree occasion, often with no sense of responsibility. *This summer let's go on a _____ and gamble in Las Vegas.*

C. ___ ___ ___ ___
   14 12 4 10

n. A group of people, often young men who cause trouble. *In "West Side Story," the Sharks were a _____ of Puerto Ricans who were fighting the Jets.*

D. ___ ___ ___
   17 15 16

n. used as an adj. A neat line of people or things, side by side. *At the theater, we sat in _____ 12, seats 5 and 6.*

E. ___ ___ ___
   6 24 13

n. A soft whitish metal, often used for cans of food. *The money was hidden in an old _____ can.*

F. ___ ___ ___
   18 8 25

n. Petroleum. *The Texans drilled a well and, at only 500 feet, struck _____.*

G. ___ ___ ___
   3 19 5

determiner. A word used in questions or negatives; some, even the smallest number or amount. *I need some money. Do you have _____?*

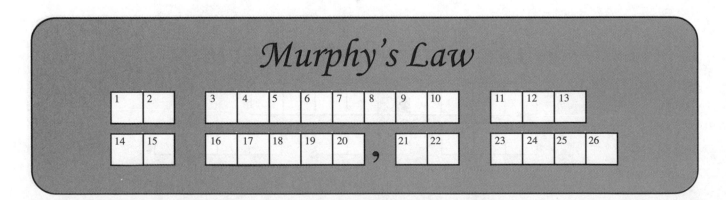

Murphy's Law

1	2		3	4	5	6	7	8	9	10		11	12	13

14	15		16	17	18	19	20	,	21	22		23	24	25	26

The Clues

A. __ __ __ __ __ __
  42 11 27 2 13 39

v. To come together. *Every Christmas Henry and Evelyn _____ around the tree with their children and sing carols.*

B. __ __ __ __ __ __
  10 29 4 14 34 26

adj. Not married; one alone. *My sister is married, but my brother is still _____.*

C. __ __ __ __ __
  31 6 37 23 5

n. The spirit of a dead person who appears again. *Alice looked frightened, as though she had seen a _____.*

D. __ __ __ __ __
  36 12 15 38 30

adj. (of a person) of full size or development; adult.. *Edgar's wife thinks that _____ men shouldn't cry.*

E. __ __ __ __ __
  32 28 7 21 3

conj. During that time. *It never fails! The telephone always rings _____ I'm taking a shower!*

F. __ __ __ __ __
  9 24 16 41 18

n. The rate of travel or advance towards an aim. *When the _____ gets tough, the tough get going.*

G. __ __ __ __
  19 33 35 22

n. A legal document in which you declare how you want your property to be shared after you die. *Albert's father died without making out a _____.*

H. __ __ __
  25 20 8

n. Adult human males. *There must be at least eleven _____ on a football team.*

I. __ __ __
  1 40 17

v. Past tense and past participle of **win**. *Yesterday Hester _____ a lot of money in the lottery.*

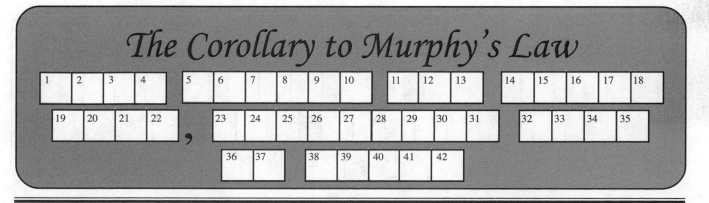

The Corollary to Murphy's Law

| 1 | 2 | 3 | 4 | 5 | 6 | 7 | 8 | 9 | 10 | 11 | 12 | 13 | 14 | 15 | 16 | 17 | 18 |

| 19 | 20 | 21 | 22 | , | 23 | 24 | 25 | 26 | 27 | 28 | 29 | 30 | 31 | 32 | 33 | 34 | 35 |

| 36 | 37 | 38 | 39 | 40 | 41 | 42 |

The Clues

A. __ __ __ __ __
  17 33 3 8 29

adj. The color of snow or milk. *In North America, the usual color of a wedding dress is _____ .*

B. __ __ __ __ __
  30 24 18 22 11

n. A small enclosed place for one person. *When you vote, you go into a voting _____ .*

C. __ __ __ __ __
  27 23 1 15 26

proper noun. The author of Tom Sawyer *and* Huckleberry Finn *was called Mark _____ .*

D. __ __ __ __
  4 31 16 21

v. To move suddenly and with great speed. *Yesterday I overslept and had to _____ to work without any breakfast.*

E. __ __ __ __
  20 28 6 13

adj. Not wide or fat; opposite of thick. *Be careful! That ice is too_____ to walk on safely.*

F. __ __ __ __
  2 10 7 14

n. A curved part, especially of a road or river. *There's a policemen hiding behind the next _____ in the road.*

G. __ __ __ __
  19 12 25 5

n. A quick, unexpected military attack. *The planes made a surprise bombing _____ on the enemy position.*

H. __ __
  32 9

interjection. A sound used to demand silence or less noise, usually whispered. *Quiet! _____! The baby is sleeping.*

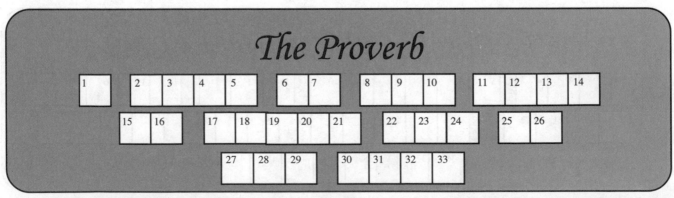

The Proverb

1		2	3	4	5		6	7		8	9	10		11	12	13	14

	15	16		17	18	19	20	21		22	23	24		25	26

	27	28	29		30	31	32	33

SOLO, DUO, TRIO: Puzzles and Games. Reproduced with permission. Copyright © 1997 by Richard Yorkey
Published by PRO LINGUA ASSOCIATES, 15 Elm Street, Brattleboro, Vermont 05301 USA 800 366 4775

Instructions

To solve this puzzle, fill in the answers to the clues, putting one letter on each numbered line. Then transfer the letters to the boxes below that have the same numbers. When all the boxes are filled in correctly, you will be able to read a common proverb in English.

The Clues

A. __ __ __ __ __ __
    9 28 12 30 10 7

n. The sky above us; also, the home of God. *Shirley was in _____ when she learned the good news that her daughter was coming home to stay.*

B. __ __ __ __ __ __
    22 11 32 26 25 20

n. A special chair for a king or queen. *Elizabeth II was only a young girl when she came to the _____ of England.*

C. __ __ __ __ __
    2 21 34 1 14

n. A common food made from flour and baked in a loaf. *I like to eat _____ and butter with my meals.*

D. __ __ __ __ __
    5 4 18 15 13

n. An opening in a sink, bathtub, or floor which leads liquids into a sewer pipe. *Please don't put tea leaves down the _____; they stop up the sink.*

E. __ __ __ __
    36 6 16 23

n. Food cooked in a particular way. *Gerald served an unusual _____ of meat and vegetables cooked in a wine sauce with mushrooms.*

F. __ __ __ __
    19 3 27 31

adj. (of weather) bright and sunny. *It's such a _____ day, let's walk instead of driving to town.*

G. __ __ __ __
    17 33 29 8

n. A kick, hit, or throw of a ball in an attempt to score a point in a game. *The forward's _____ went to the right of the goal.*

H. __ __
    24 35

proper noun. Abbreviation of an organization that helps people who are alcoholics. *Mary was so happy when her son finally agreed to get help from _____.*

The Proverb

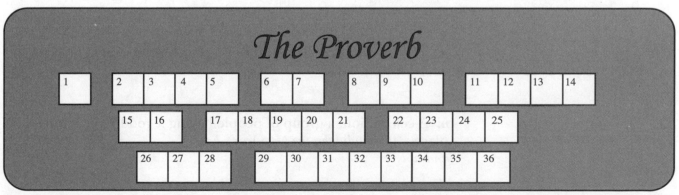

SOLO, DUO, TRIO: Puzzles and Games. Reproduced with permission. Copyright © 1997 by Richard Yorkey
Published by PRO LINGUA ASSOCIATES, 15 Elm Street, Brattleboro, Vermont 05301 USA 800 366 4775

A Double-Crostic Puzzle #12

The Clues

A. __ __ __ __ __ __
23 12 7 27 34 5

adj. Well-known. *Elvis Presley was a _____ rock and roll star.*

B. __ __ __ __ __
31 3 45 41 20

v. To express amusement or happiness with a forceful sound of your voice, usually while smiling. *I always _____ at the old movies of Charlie Chaplin.*

C. __ __ __ __ __
28 13 50 32 51

n. The brother of your mother or father. *My aunt and _____ visited me yesterday.*

D __ __ __ __ __
8 24 10 35 43

n. A celebration; a group of people having a good time in one place. *After midnight, the New Year's Eve _____ became very wild and noisy.*

SOLO, DUO, TRIO: Puzzles and Games. Reproduced with permission. Copyright © 1997 by Richard Yorkey
Published by PRO LINGUA ASSOCIATES, 15 Elm Street, Brattleboro, Vermont 05301 USA 800 366 4775

Here are more clues. When you have finished the clues and written the numbered letters into the boxes below, an important truth about life will be revealed to you.

E. _ _ _ _ _
  29 40 25 16 4

adj. At the beginning; before anything else. *The letter A is the _____ letter of the English alphabet.*

F. _ _ _ _ _
  46 37 18 14 36

n. A small enclosed place for one person. *In our language lab, each student sits in a _____ with earphones and a tape recorder.*

G. _ _ _ _
  22 30 49 19

v. To wish for or desire. *I _____ to learn English as quickly as possible.*

H. _ _ _ _
  11 39 6 17

adj. Not wide or fat. *Mary looks much too _____. I don't think she's eating enough.*

I. _ _ _
  1 42 9

interrogative. What person or persons. *Do you know _____ wrote* Romeo and Juliet?

J. _ _ _
  33 47 26

n. A male child. *The Martins have four children. They had three girls and then a _____.*

K. _ _ _
  15 44 48

n. A piece of paper saying that someone owes you a certain amount of money. *I haven't any cash right now. Will you accept an _____?*

L. _ _ _
  2 21 38

adv. In what way. *_____ do you spell your name?*

An Important Truth about Life

1	2	3	4	, 5		6	7	8	9	10	11	12	13	14

| 15 | 16 | | 17 | 18 | 19 | | 20 | 21 | 22 | | 23 | 24 | 25 | | 26 | 27 | 28 |

| 29 | 30 | 31 | 32 | | 33 | 34 | 35 | | 36 | 37 | 38 | | 39 | 40 | 41 | 42 |

| 43 | 44 | 45 | | 46 | 47 | 48 | 49 | 50 | 51 |

Answers for the Double-Crostic Puzzles

#1   Curiosity killed the cat.
A. style
B. thick
C. road
D. cute
E. LII

#2   Absence makes the heart grow fonder.
A. semester
B. change
C. heard
D. fork
E. town
F. Abe

#3   Speech is silver but silence is golden.
A. visitor
B. spell
C. since
D. child
E. seen
F. use
G. beg

#4   Don't put all your eggs in one basket.
A. largest
B. sound
C. page
D. like
E. buy
F. ton
G. not

#5   Don't count your chickens before they hatch.
A. her
B. buy
C. the
D. toy
E. noon
F. dock
G. trust
H. chief
I. chance

#6   If wishes were horses, beggars would ride.
A. fog
B. sew
C. bad
D. wise
E. users
F. error
G. weigh
H. shield

#7   Talk less and say more.
A. Yale
B. sank
C. least
D. dorms

#8   If anything can go wrong, it will.
A. witch
B. fling
C. gang
D. row
E. tin
F. oil
G. any

#9   When things are going well, something will go wrong.
A. gather
B. single
C. ghost
D. grown
E. while
F. going
G. will
H. men
I. won

#10 A bird in the hand is worth two in the bush.
A. white
B. booth
C. Twain
D. rush
E. thin
F. bend
G. raid
H. Sh

#11 A bird in the hand is safer than one overhead.
A. heaven
B. throne
C. bread
D. drain
E. dish
F. fine
G. shot
H. AA

#12 What's important is not how far you fall but how high you bounce.
A. famous
B. laugh
C. uncle
D. party
E. first
F. booth
G. want
H. thin
I. who
J. boy
K. IOU
L. how

Odd One Out

Instructions

In each list of five words, one word does not belong, because it is somehow different from the others. Circle the number of the word and explain why it does not belong.

Example A
1. red
2. paint
3. yellow
4. blue
5. orange

Reason: *Paint is not the name of a color.*

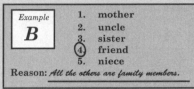

Example B
1. mother
2. uncle
3. sister
4. friend
5. niece

Reason: *All the others are family members.*

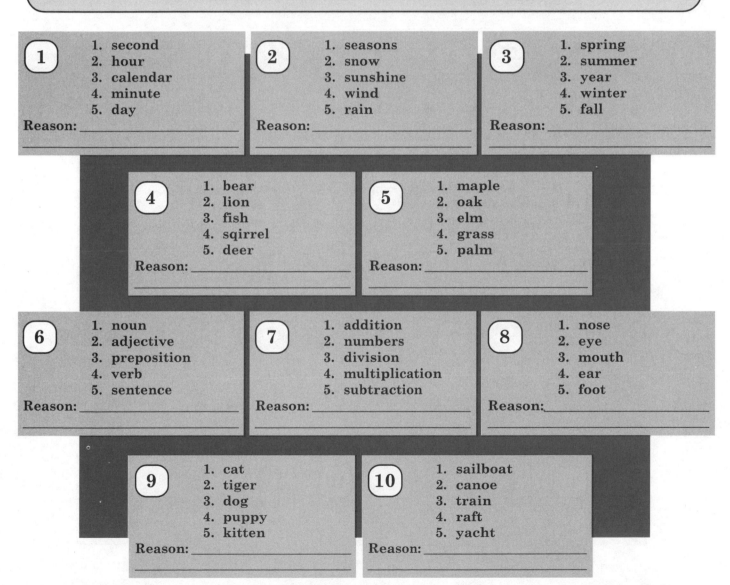

1.
1. second
2. hour
3. calendar
4. minute
5. day

Reason: _____

2.
1. seasons
2. snow
3. sunshine
4. wind
5. rain

Reason: _____

3.
1. spring
2. summer
3. year
4. winter
5. fall

Reason: _____

4.
1. bear
2. lion
3. fish
4. sqirrel
5. deer

Reason: _____

5.
1. maple
2. oak
3. elm
4. grass
5. palm

Reason: _____

6.
1. noun
2. adjective
3. preposition
4. verb
5. sentence

Reason: _____

7.
1. addition
2. numbers
3. division
4. multiplication
5. subtraction

Reason: _____

8.
1. nose
2. eye
3. mouth
4. ear
5. foot

Reason: _____

9.
1. cat
2. tiger
3. dog
4. puppy
5. kitten

Reason: _____

10.
1. sailboat
2. canoe
3. train
4. raft
5. yacht

Reason: _____

Odd One Out

Instructions

In each list of five words, one word does not belong, because it is somehow different from the others. Circle the number of the word and explain why it does not belong.

Example A		Example B	
1. red		1. mother	
②. paint		2. uncle	
3. yellow		3. sister	
4. blue		④ friend	
5. orange		5. niece	

Reason: *Paint is not the name of a color.*

Reason: *All the others are family members.*

1
1. racquet
2. lens
3. film
4. photograph
5. camera

Reason: _____
_____

2
1. golf
2. walking
3. football
4. tennis
5. bowling

Reason: _____
_____

3
1. noon
2. sunset
3. dawn
4. sky
5. night

Reason: _____
_____

4
1. triangle
2. distance
3. square
4. circle
5. cone

Reason: _____
_____

5
1. ruler
2. pencil
3. pen
4. school
5. paper

Reason: _____
_____

6
1. earthquake
2. tornado
3. flood
4. hurricane
5. shelter

Reason: _____
_____

7
1. candy
2. bag
3. box
4. package
5. jar

Reason: _____
_____

8
1. teacher
2. architect
3. chef
4. mechanic
5. thief

Reason: _____
_____

9
1. house
2. apartment
3. bank
4. cabin
5. tent

Reason: _____
_____

10
1. star
2. comet
3. moon
4. space
5. sun

Reason: _____
_____

Odd One Out

Instructions

In each list of five words, one word does not belong, because it is somehow different from the others. Circle the number of the word and explain why it does not belong.

Example A
1. red
2. paint *(circled)*
3. yellow
4. blue
5. orange

Reason: *Paint is not the name of a color.*

Example B
1. mother
2. uncle
3. sister
4. friend *(circled)*
5. niece

Reason: *All the others are family members.*

1
1. Spain
2. Katmandu
3. Chad
4. India
5. Guatemala

Reason: _____

2
1. $100.00
2. $50.00
3. $25.00
4. $1.00
5. $10.00

Reason: _____

3
1. waltz
2. tango
3. rumba
4. music
5. fox trot

Reason: _____

4
1. violin
2. cello
3. harp
4. viola
5. clarinet

Reason: _____

5
1. John Kennedy
2. Elvis Presley
3. Abraham Lincoln
4. Franklin Roosevelt
5. George Bush

Reason: _____

6
1. R
2. E
3. I
4. A
5. O

Reason: _____

7
1. Montreal
2. Manila
3. Amsterdam
4. London
5. Panama

Reason: _____

8
1. Latin
2. Spanish
3. Portuguese
4. Japanese
5. French

Reason: _____

9
1. polite
2. kind
3. helpful
4. selfish
5. considerate

Reason: _____

10
1. oven
2. bathtub
3. refrigerator
4. sink
5. microwave

Reason: _____

SOLO, DUO, TRIO: Puzzles and Games. Reproduced with permission. Copyright © 1997 by Richard Yorkey
Published by PRO LINGUA ASSOCIATES, 15 Elm Street, Brattleboro, Vermont 05301 USA 800 366 4775

Answers for
Odd One Out

#1

1. **calendar**
   The other words are units of time during the day.
2. **seasons**
   The other words are weather words.
3. **year**
   The other words are the names of seasons.
4. **fish**
   The other words are the names of land animals.
5. **grass**
   The other words are the names of trees.
6. **sentence**
   The other words are parts of speech.
7. **numbers**
   The other words are arithmetic operations
8. **foot**
   The other words name parts of the head (or face).
9. **tiger**
   The other words are the names of domestic (tame) animals or family pets.
10. **train**
    The other words name kinds of boats (water craft).

#2

1. **raquet**
   The other words have to do with photography.
2. **walking**
   The other words are the names of sports that need a ball.
3. **sky**
   The other words refer to times of day.
4. **distance**
   The other words refer to geometic shapes.
5. **school**
   The other words are things in a classroom (school).
6. **shelter**
   The other words are natural disasters.
7. **candy**
   The other words are containers (for candy).
8. **thief**
   The other words are professions (career jobs).
9. **bank**
   The other words are places where people live.
10. **space**
    The other words refer to astronomical bodies.

#3

1. **Katmandu**
   The other words are the names of countries. Katmandu is the capital city of Nepal.
2. **$25.00**
   The other words refer to amounts of money for which there is a U.S. bill. There is no $25 bill.
3. **music**
   The other words are names of dances.
   fox trot
   The other words are single word musical terms
4. **clarinet**
   The other words are names of string instruments. The clarinet is a woodwind.
5. **Elvis Presley**
   The other people were all American presidents. Elvis was a "king" but no president.
   Abraham Lincoln
   The other people lived in the 20th Century.
6. **R**   *The other letters are vowels.*
7. **Panama**
   The other words are the names of cities. Panama City (Pamama's capital) is only informally called "Panama."
8. **Latin**
   The other words are names of living languages.
   Japanese
   The other languages are of European origin.
9. **selfish**
   The other adjectives describe positive attributes.
10. **bathtub**
    The other words refer to things ordinarly in the kitchen. Also, bathtub is the only compound word.

✎ A Word Square Puzzle #1

Instructions

Each numbered definition below is followed by a sample sentence with one missing word. The number after the definition is the number of letters in the word you want. Write the missing word in the word square. Start at square number 1 with the word from definition 1. The last letter of each word is the first letter of the next. Examples:

1. The coldest season of the year. {6 letters} *It snows in the __winter__ .*
2. A flowering bush with thorns. *{4}* "A __rose__ by any other name would smell as sweet."

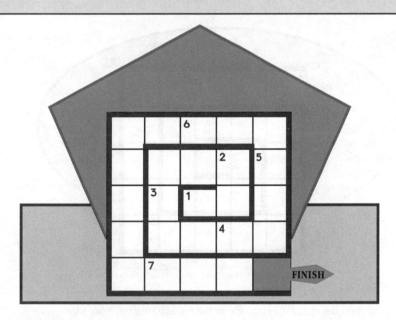

1. Large. {3 letters} *Henry is a _ _ _ boy for his age.*

2. Right, satisfactory. {4} *The party was enjoyable and everybody had a _ _ _ _ time.*

3. A table used for studying or writing. {4} *I always keep a dictionary on my _ _ _ _ at home.*

4. A man who wears a crown and rules a country. {4} *Richard I was the _ _ _ _ of England during the Crusades.*

5. A female child. {4} *All the boys like Barbara because she is such a pretty little _ _ _ _ .*

6. Human speech. {8} *Spanish is the _ _ _ _ _ _ _ _ that is spoken in Mexico.*

7. The way out of a place. {4} *Be sure to know where the _ _ _ _ is just in case of a fire.*

SOLO, DUO, TRIO: Puzzles and Games. Reproduced with permission. Copyright © 1997 by Richard Yorkey
Published by PRO LINGUA ASSOCIATES, 15 Elm Street, Brattleboro, Vermont 05301 USA 800 366 4775

✎ A Word Square Puzzle #2

Instructions

Each numbered definition below is followed by a sample sentence with one missing word. The number after the definition is the number of letters in the word you want. Write the missing word in the word square. Start at square number 1 with the word from definition 1. The last letter of each word is the first letter of the next. Examples:

1. The coldest season of the year. {6 letters} *It snows in the* __winter__ .

2. A flowering bush with thorns. {4} *"A* __rose__ *by any other name would smell as sweet."*

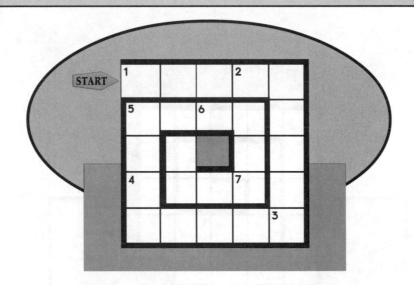

1. One of two equal parts. {4 letters} *Jason cut the cupcake in the middle and gave his wife* _ _ _ _ .

2. Someone whom you know well and like to be with. {6} *In school my best* _ _ _ _ _ _ *and I never fought or had any kind of disagreement.*

3. One hundred cents. {6} *A picture of George Washington is on the one-* _ _ _ _ _ _ *bill.*

4. The color of blood and fire engines. {3} *Six of the thirteen stripes on the American flag are white; the others are* _ _ _ .

5. A large four-legged animal that is often kept as a pet. {3} *Eddie was afraid when he heard the* _ _ _ *bark.*

6. An activity that is played according to certain rules; a sports contest. {4} *For his birthday, Helen took her husband to a baseball* _ _ _ _ .

7. The world; this planet. {5} *The* _ _ _ _ _ *moves around the sun.*

A Word Square Puzzle #3

Instructions

Each numbered definition below is followed by a sample sentence with one missing word. The number after the definition is the number of letters in the word you want. Write the missing word in the word square. Start at square number 1 with the word from definition 1. The last letter of each word is the first letter of the next. Examples:

1. The coldest season of the year. {6 letters} *It snows in the ___winter___ .*
2. A flowering bush with thorns. *{4} "A __rose__ by any other name would smell as sweet."*

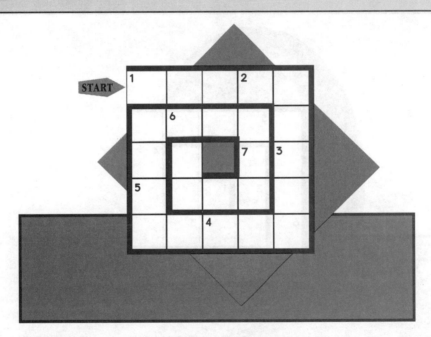

1. An infant; a very young child who cannot walk or talk yet. {4 letters} *Carolyn's _ _ _ _ is only five weeks old.*

2. A time period of 12 months or 365 days. {4} *On December 31, everyone looks forward to the new _ _ _ _ .*

3. Agreeing with the facts; correct. {5} *Paul had only one wrong answer on his test; all the other answers with _ _ _ _ _ _ .*

4. A tall, woody plant with a main stem from which branches grow. {4} *A large maple _ _ _ _ shades my house.*

5. A compass direction, the opposite of west. {4} *The sun always rises in the _ _ _ _ .*

6. Very high. {5} *Although George is two years younger than Phil, he is as _ _ _ _ as his brother.*

7. To try to hear someone or something. {6} *Sally didn't want to _ _ _ _ _ _ to what her mother was telling her.*

SOLO, DUO, TRIO: Puzzles and Games. Reproduced with permission. Copyright © 1997 by Richard Yorkey
Published by PRO LINGUA ASSOCIATES, 15 Elm Street, Brattleboro, Vermont 05301 USA 800 366 4775

Each numbered definition below is followed by a sample sentence with one missing word. The number after the definition is the number of letters in the word you want. Write the missing word in the word square. Start at square number 1 with the word from definition 1. The last letter of each word is the first letter of the next. Examples:

1. The coldest season of the year. {6 letters} *It snows in the ___winter___ .*
2. A flowering bush with thorns. {4} *"A __rose__ by any other name would smell as sweet."*

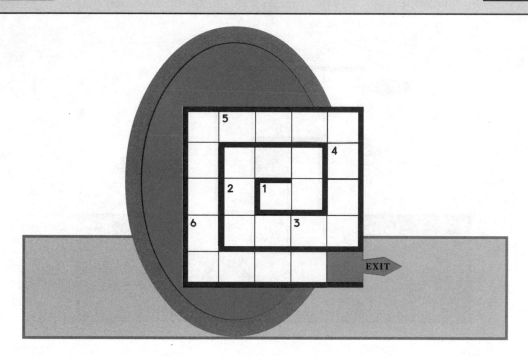

1. Not to remember. {6 letters} *I can't remember my own telephone number! Why do I always _ _ _ _ _ _ it?*

2. Correct, not false; real. {4} *It is difficult to believe that English is spoken by almost half a billion people, but it's _ _ _ _ .*

3. Not difficult. {4} *This puzzle is simple. It should be very ˜ _ _ _ to do.*

4. In the early years of life. {5} *Our mother was too _ _ _ _ _ to remember when JFK was shot.*

5. The color of grass and leaves in the springtime. {5} *After a cold, snowy winter, it is a real pleasure to see _ _ _ _ _ grass again!*

6. A written or spoken figure telling how many. {6} *Six is a larger _ _ _ _ _ _ than five.*

✎ A Word Square Puzzle #5

Instructions

Each numbered definition below is followed by a sample sentence with one missing word. Write the missing word in the word square. The number after the definition is the number of letters in the word you want. Start at square number 1 with the word from definition 1. The last letter of each word is the first letter of the next. Examples:

1. The coldest season of the year. {6 letters} *It snows in the* **winter**.

2. A flowering bush with thorns. *{4}* "*A* **rose** *by any other name would smell as sweet.*"

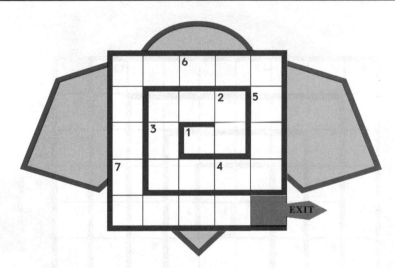

EXIT

1. Work, employment. {3 letters} *Michael's _ _ _ pays only a minimum wage.*

2. A small vessel that floats on the water. *{4} In the storm our fishing _ _ _ _ filled with water and sank.*

3. To speak, to say something. {4} *Mary told her husband not to _ _ _ _ to her while she was watching the football game.*

4. To understand and be able to use something; to be certain. {4} *Chuy asked, "How many languages does Estella _ _ _ _?"*

   "I don't _ _ _ _ for sure," Lee Sung replied. "At least five, I think."

5. Something built of wood, bricks, or other material to enclose a space, like the sides of a room or building. {4} *One _ _ _ _ of the room was painted white and the others were painted blue.*

6. The distance from one end to the other; how long something is. {6} *The width of the room is twelve feet, and its _ _ _ _ _ _ is twenty-five feet.*

7. How your body feels; the condition of being free from illness. {6} *Oscar was always in good _ _ _ _ _ _ until he got cancer.*

 # A Word Square Puzzle #6

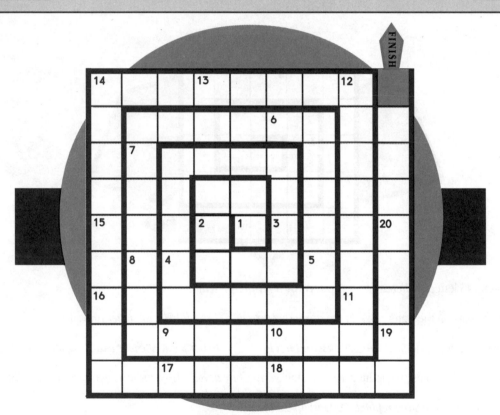

1. To wish that something may happen although you know it may not. {4 letters} *My parents* _ _ _ _ *that I will be a successful*

   brain surgeon.

2. To be; to continue to live. {5} *We need air and water to* _ _ _ _ _ .

3. To express the meaning of words in one language in the words of another language. {9} *Who can* _ _ _ _ _ _ _ _ _ *the word*

   dictionary into Japanese so that Kenji can understand?

Continued on the next page.

SOLO, DUO, TRIO: Puzzles and Games. Reproduced with permission. Copyright © 1997 by Richard Yorkey
Published by PRO LINGUA ASSOCIATES, 15 Elm Street, Brattleboro, Vermont 05301 USA 800 366 4775

Continue writing the missing words from the sentences below into the word square puzzle until you reach the colored square. That is the end.

4. To tell what the meaning is; to make something clear. {7 letters} *The teacher had to _ _ _ _ _ _ _ the meaning of present*

perfect tense.

5. To watch carefully; to observe. {6} *The chemistry teacher told his students to _ _ _ _ _ _ what happened when he added*

copper sulfate to the solution.

6. To think that something will happen. {6} *We _ _ _ _ _ _ Ingrid to come home from college any day now.*

7. To speak; to say something. {4} *It is impolite to _ _ _ _ during a movie or a play.*

8. To continue or stay as something is. {4} *Don't get excited during an emergency. Try to _ _ _ _ calm and think clearly.*

9. To use force against something for the purpose of moving it. {4} *When Herman's car ran out of gas, he had to get out and*

_ _ _ _ it to the nearest gas station.

10. To use your ears to listen to sounds. {4} *The teacher didn't speak very loudly, so it was difficult to _ _ _ _ what she said.*

11. To ask for something. {7} *Mr. and Mrs. Arthur Brown _ _ _ _ _ _ _ the pleasure of your company at the wedding of their*

daughter, Marie....

12. To express gratitude to someone. {5} *I want to _ _ _ _ _ you for your kindness in helping me while I was sick.*

13. To take the life of any living thing. {4} *Cigarettes _ _ _ _ thousands of people every year by causing lung cancer.*

14. To go away; depart. {5} *The train didn't _ _ _ _ _ the station until 3:30 p.m.*

15. To chew and swallow food. {3} *Children like to _ _ _ ice cream and cake.*

16. To give lessons; instruct; to help someone learn. {5} *Henry's illness may _ _ _ _ _ him the dangers of smoking.*

17. To aid or assist; to make something easier for someone to do. {4} *Paul asked his teacher to _ _ _ _ him understand the*

meaning of **unique**.

18. To push against or down on something. {5} *DIRECTIONS: If you want to erase what is on the screen, _ _ _ _ _ the delete key.*

19. To point out; to allow something to be seen. {4} *I want to see your new car. Please _ _ _ _ it to me now.*

20. To form letters and words with a pen, pencil, or word processor so that people can read what your name. {5}

Be sure to _ _ _ _ _ your name on your test paper before you hand it in.

A Word Square Puzzle #7

Instructions

Each numbered definition below is followed by a sample sentence with one missing word. The number after the definition is the number of letters in the word you want. Write the missing word in the word square. Start at square number 1 with the word from definition 1. The last letter of each word is the first letter of the next. Examples:

1. The coldest season of the year. {6 letters} *It snows in the __winter__.*
2. A flowering bush with thorns. {4} *"A __rose__ by any other name would smell as sweet."*

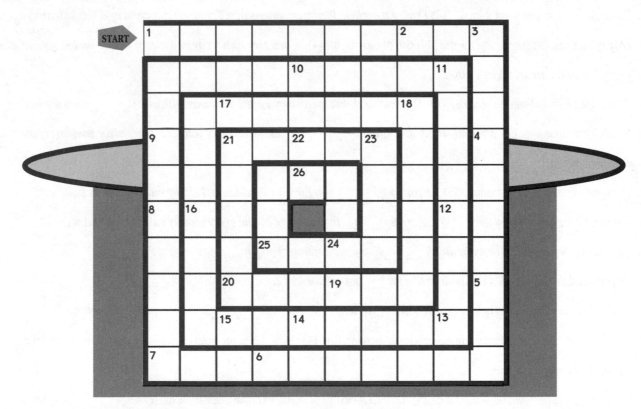

START

1. The last month of the year. {8 letters} *Christmas is celebrated in the month of _ _ _ _ _ _ _ _.*

2. A large mouse. {3} *Mary screamed when the _ _ _ ran across the room.*

3. A group of people helping each other on a job or in a sport. {4} *There are five players on a basketball _ _ _ _.*

4. To walk in step. {5} *Soldiers have to _ _ _ _ _ in a parade.*

5. Great joy. {9} *There is no greater _ _ _ _ _ _ _ _ _ than a good marriage.*

Continued on the next page.

Instructions

Continue writing the missing words from the sentences below into the word square puzzle until you reach the colored square. That is the end.

6. To finish doing something. {4 letters} *Please _ _ _ _ talking so loudly in the library.*

7. A large musical instrument with a keyboard. {5} *Mozart could play the _ _ _ _ _ when he was only four years old.*

8. A preposition, opposite of <u>on</u>. {3} *The book fell _ _ _ the table.*

9. Toward the front. {7} *In the spring time we have to move the clock _ _ _ _ _ _ _ an hour.*

10. To put clothes on. {5} *Little Billy can _ _ _ _ _ himself.*

11. Little. {5} *John is very _ _ _ _ _ for his age.*

12. A device, usually electric, that gives light. {4} *The bulb in the _ _ _ _ beside my bed went out.*

13. A juicy, round fruit with a soft, yellowish-red skin and a hard pit. {5} *I like to slice a _ _ _ _ _ on my breakfast cereal.*

14. Very warm. {3} *Because of the sun, it's too _ _ _ to do anything but sit and try to stay cool.*

15. The short, thick finger of the hand. {5} *Philip accidentally slammed the car door on his _ _ _ _ _ .*

16. A round, soft cap with a full, flat top. {5} *My French friend always wears a _ _ _ _ _ on his head.*

17. A game played with racquets and a ball on a court with a net. {6} *An important international _ _ _ _ _ _ tournament is played every year at Wimbledon.*

18. A cutting tool with two knives fastened together in the middle {8} *I need a pair of _ _ _ _ _ _ _ _ to cut this paper into smaller pieces.*

19. Water in the cold air that freezes into flakes as it falls. {4} *With more than a foot of new-fallen _ _ _ _ , the skiing will be excellent.*

20. H_2O {5} *You should drink at least eight glasses of _ _ _ _ _ a day.*

21. The color of blood. {3} *You mix yellow and _ _ _ to make orange.*

22. A four-legged animal kept as a pet, or used for hunting, working, or guarding. {3} *I could hear my neighbor's _ _ _ barking all night.*

23. A transparent, solid material that is breakable. *{5} Harry dropped his _ _ _ _ _ of beer, and it shattered into many pieces.*

24. To slide over snow on two long pieces of wood. {3} *I like to _ _ _ downhill rather than cross-country.*

25. The capital of this Middle Eastern nation is Baghdad. {4} *Biblical Babylon is now the country of _ _ _ _ .*

26. A short, informal test. {4} *Be sure to study the new vocabulary, because there will be a _ _ _ _ tomorrow.*

 # A Word Square Puzzle #8

1. The coldest season of the year. {6 letters} *It snows in the* __*winter*__ .

2. A flowering bush with thorns. *{4}* *"A* __*rose*__ *by any other name would smell as sweet."*

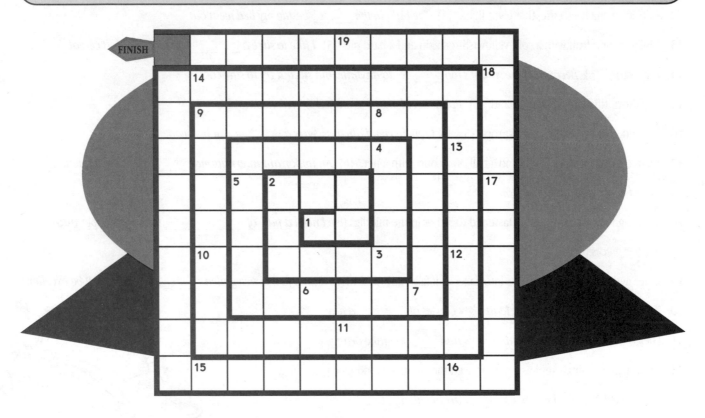

1. A large sea with salty water. {5 letters} *The Pacific _ _ _ _ _ is larger than the Atlantic.*

2. Words or symbols to show the order or quantity of things. {6} *The _ _ _ _ _ _ between 5 and 7 is 6.*

3. Wealthy. {4} *People who are _ _ _ _ can afford expensive homes and cars.*

4. Feeling the need or desire for food. {6} *No wonder the child is so _ _ _ _ _ _ ! She hasn't eaten anything since yesterday.*

5. The color of a lemon or a banana. {6} *A buttercup is a _ _ _ _ _ _ flower.*

Continued on the next page.

Continue writing the missing words from the sentences below into the word square puzzle until you reach the colored square. That is the end.

6. Seven days. {4 letters} *Tomorrow is a holiday, but we have classes all of next _ _ _ _.*

7. A room in which cooking is done. {7} *If you can't stand the heat, get out of the _ _ _ _ _ _ _.*

8. A group of people united under one government; a country. {6} *The United States is a _ _ _ _ _ _ of 50 states.*

9. A direction, opposite of south. {5} *Winters in the United States and Canada are colder in the _ _ _ _ _ than in the south.*

10. The number 100. {7} *In the United States each of the fifty states has two senators; therefore, there are a _ _ _ _ _ _ _ senators in the U.S. Senate.*

11. A person trained in medicine; a physician. {6} *When I broke my arm, I went to a _ _ _ _ _ _ at our local hospital.*

12. A narrow circle of metal, often gold or silver, worn on a finger. {4} *The bride proudly showed off her new wedding _ _ _ _.*

13. The people and organization in power to make laws. {10} *The United States _ _ _ _ _ _ _ _ _ _ is located in Washington, DC.*

14. The degree of heat or cold, measured on a Fahrenheit or Celsius scale. {11} *The average winter _ _ _ _ _ _ _ _ _ _ _ in Vermont is 17° F.*

15. All persons. {8} *_ _ _ _ _ _ _ _ in this class is learning English as a Second Language.*

16. The time between sunset and night. {7} *Children usually go to bed early in the _ _ _ _ _ _ _.*

17. A precious yellow metal. {4} *In 1848 _ _ _ _ was discovered in California.*

18. A dry area, covered with sand and without water or vegetation. {6} *Camels are useful animals for crossing the _ _ _ _ _ _.*

19. A small piece of paper or cardboard that proves you have the right to a seat in a theater, bus, train, or airplane. {6} *I have just enough money to buy a _ _ _ _ _ _ for the football game.*

SOLO, DUO, TRIO: Puzzles and Games. Reproduced with permission. Copyright © 1997 by Richard Yorkey
Published by PRO LINGUA ASSOCIATES, 15 Elm Street, Brattleboro, Vermont 05301 USA 800 366 4775

✏️ A Word Square Puzzle #9

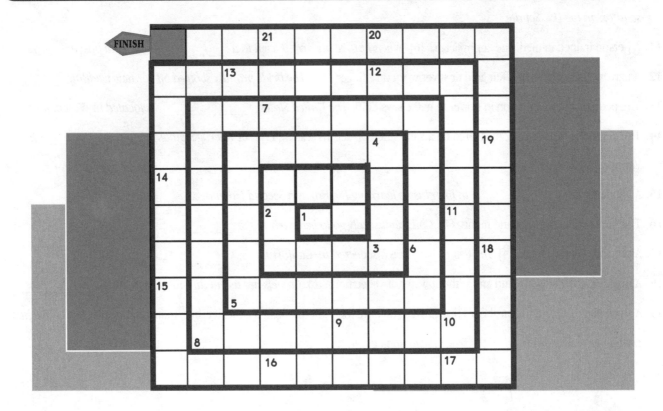

1. Tired; in need of sleep. {6 letters} *The lecture was so boring that the students felt too* _ _ _ _ _ _ *to stay awake.*

2. Not old. {5} *Mary is too* _ _ _ _ _ *to drive. She has another year before she can get a license.*

3. Better than average. {4} *Paul is not the best student in the class, but he's a* _ _ _ _ *student who does satisfactory work.*

4. Not safe; causing harm. {9} *The machine is* _ _ _ _ _ _ _ _ _ *because the electrical wiring is faulty.*

Continued on the next page.

Instructions

Continue writing the missing words from the sentences below into the word square puzzle until you reach the colored square. That is the end.

5. Unusual; unfamiliar. {7 letters} *When Oscar travels in foreign countries, he enjoys learning about the _ _ _ _ _ _ _ food and customs of the people.*

6. Costing a lot; very high-priced. {9} *A Cadillac is more _ _ _ _ _ _ _ _ _ than a Ford.*

7. Better than others; very good. {9} *At the end of the English course, Hilda's work was _ _ _ _ _ _ _ _ _, so she was awarded a prize for being The Most Improved Student.*

8. Not thin. {5} *Eduardo wears a _ _ _ _ _, bushy moustache.*

9. Friendly; gentle. {4} *Helping the old woman across the street was a _ _ _ _ thing to do.*

10. Measuring a great distance downward; not shallow. {4} *The ocean is very _ _ _ _ off the coast of South America.*

11. Well liked; having many friends. {7} *Elvis Presley was a _ _ _ _ _ _ _ rock 'n' roll singer.*

12. Uneven; not smooth. {5} *A Jeep is a good vehicle for driving over _ _ _ _ _ terrain.*

13. Having a hole within; empty. {6} *The fox was able to hide in a _ _ _ _ _ _ tree.*

14. Having or feeling a small amount of heat. {4} *In winter we have to wear _ _ _ _ clothing.*

15. New; up to date. {6} *Our office has all the _ _ _ _ _ _ conveniences for business and communication.*

16. Usual; standard. {6} *The _ _ _ _ _ _ temperature for a person is 98.6°F.*

17. Not heavy; having little substance. {5} *Helen was wearing a very _ _ _ _ _ coat for such cold weather.*

18. Not thick {4} *Henry is dieting so that he can be _ _ _ _ again.*

19. Not learned or acquired; true to nature. {7} *It is _ _ _ _ _ _ _ for parents to love their children.*

20. Measuring more than usual from one end to the other; not short. {4} *It's a _ _ _ _ distance from New York to San Francisco.*

21. Pleased; happy. {4} *I was _ _ _ _ to see so many of my friends at graduation.*

Answers for the Word Square Puzzles

#1
big
good
desk
king
girl
language
exit

#2
half
friend
dollar
red
dog
game
earth

#3
baby
year
right
tree
east
tall
listen

#4
forget
true
easy
young
green
number

#5
job
boat
talk
know
wall
length
health

#6
hope
exist
translate
explain
notice
expect
talk
keep
push
hear

request
thank
kill
leave
eat
teach
help
press
show
write

#7
December
rat
team
march
happiness
stop
piano
off
forward
dress
small
lamp
peach
hot
thumb
beret

tennis
scissors
snow
water
red
dog
glass
ski
Iraq
quiz

#8
ocean
number
rich
hungry
yellow
week
kitchen
nation
north
hundred
doctor
ring
government
temperature
everyone
evening

gold
desert
ticket

#9
sleepy
young
good
dangerous
strange
expensive
excellent
thick
kind
deep
popular
rough
hollow
warm
modern
normal
light
thin
natural
long
glad

✎ A Cloze Word Puzzle #1

⇨ ACROSS ⇨

1. The speaker sounded as _ _ _ _ _ _ he had a sore throat.

7. The country has its _ _ _ oil, so it doesn't need to import any.

8. Of the four choices below the question, only _ _ _ is the correct answer.

10. You want $100 for your old typewriter, and I'm offering you $80. Why don't we _ _ _ _ _ the difference and agree on $90. Okay?

12. Most airplane accidents happen during either the take-off _ _ the landing.

13. There are many more small _ _ _ _ _ than big cities in a country.

Continued on the next page.

15. The judge ordered the prisoner to _ _ sent to jail for one year.

16. While weeding the garden, Henry broke the handle of his _ _ _.

17. I _ _ _ _ _ _ work in Chicago, but I don't anymore. *[TWO WORDS]*

20. The mayor was at the front of the big parade, which he _ _ _ down the street to Town Hall.

21. What would you do _ _ you had a million dollars?

22. Hurry! We better _ _ _ _ across the street now before the light changes.

23. The hunter took careful aim and shot _ _ the bird – but missed!

⇩ DOWN ⇩

2. Henry twisted his ankle during basketball practice and had to _ _ _ on one foot all the way home.

3. With its large eyes, an _ _ _ is a strange-looking bird; I don't know why it's supposed to be so wise.

4. There are fifty states in the _ _ _ _ _ _ States of America.

5. This word is either a third of Santa Claus's laugh or the first part of "_ _-hum," an expression you might use when you're tired or bored.

6. Barbara stared at _ _ _ _ _ _ _ in the mirror and saw how much she had aged.

9. Shouting or speaking in a loud voice in a library is a _ _ _-_ _. *[TWO WORDS, HYPHENATED]*

10. _ _ _ _ _ _ you need any help, please don't hesitate to call me.

11. Alfred hoped to get at least one of the jobs he applied for. But, _ _ his great surprise, he was offered both!

14. If Cynthia isn't willing, let's offer the chance to someone _ _ _ is.

15. Longwood Gardens has so many beautiful _ _ _ _ of flowers, each one carefully weeded and watered.

18. On the first day at _ _ _ , Paul always gets sick from the ship's motion.

19. The sign of the infinitive is the little word _ _.

21. Helen was very frightened, but she tried not to show _ _.

SOLO, DUO, TRIO: Puzzles and Games. Reproduced with permission. Copyright © 1997 by Richard Yorkey
Published by PRO LINGUA ASSOCIATES, 15 Elm Street, Brattleboro, Vermont 05301 USA 800 366 4775

A Cloze Word Puzzle

Instructions

The words that fit into this kind of puzzle have been left out of the sentences given below and replaced by broken lines. Try to guess the words from clues in the context; you are not given definitions of the words. Each small blank in the broken line represents one letter in the missing word.(or words). When you guess a word, write it into the puzzle starting in the square with the same number as the number of the clue sentence. For example, the word missing in sentence "1 across" is written across ⇨ the puzzle starting in square 1. The word from sentence "2 down" is written from square 2 down ⇩ .

⇨ ACROSS ⇨

1. When I'm nervous, I _ _ _ _ my fingernails.

4. The thief ran away too _ _ _ _ and the police officer couldn't catch him.

7. When the workers heard that the factory was going to be closed and they would all be out
   of a job, they were furious and it was hard for them to control their _ _ _ _ _ _.

8. King _ _ _ _ was a huge gorilla who climbed the Empire State Building with his beloved woman in
   his hand.

10. It's not very _ _ _ _ to stay up late the night before an important exam in school.

SOLO, DUO, TRIO: Puzzles and Games. Reproduced with permission. Copyright © 1997 by Richard Yorkey
Published by PRO LINGUA ASSOCIATES, 15 Elm Street, Brattleboro, Vermont 05301 USA 800 366 4775

12. An _ _ _ is a very large deer with big antlers.

14. Henry was so hungry he _ _ _ two Big Macs and a large French fries.

15. The holiday season is a time of great _ _ _ because our whole family gets together.

16. The _ _ _ that clings to the walls of their buildings shows how old Harvard, Yale, and Princeton are.

18. My father always told me, "Don't put off till tomorrow what you can do today. Do it _ _ _!"

20. The auditorium was completely full. There wasn't a single empty _ _ _ _.

22. In church, Barbara always worries about her _ _ _ _ part when she has to sing alone, without the choir or organ accompaniment.

23. Paul works in a factory where he just repeats the same action over and over on the assembly line; he thinks a _ _ _ _ _ could perform the work just as easily and probably better than he can.

24. The little paper boat was caught in an _ _ _ _ and spun around and around in the water.

25. Susan never seems to have enough money. She's always up to her _ _ _ _ in debt.

⇩ DOWN ⇩

1. Our oven wasn't working, so my mother couldn't _ _ _ _ a cake for my birthday; she had to buy one from the bakery.

2. It takes 15 gallons of water to fill my fish _ _ _ _.

3. In the college catalog, the Modern English Grammar course is abbreviated Mn _ _ _ Gr.

4. Very _ _ _ people can fully understand Einstein's Theory of Relativity.

5. In the opera *La Boheme*, Rodolfo sings a beautiful _ _ _ _, "Che gelida manina."

6. Because there are still so many of them growing in the mountains, the cedar _ _ _ _ is the national symbol of Lebanon.

9. An _ _ _ _ _ branch is a traditional sign of peace.

11. When we had to move our heavy piano, my father and I pushed it, and my brother helped by picking up the piano _ _ _ _ _!

13. Carolyn and her sister were naughty and ate a whole _ _ _ of chocolate candy before supper.

16. Hector met his wife while visiting the _ _ _ _ of Capri off the coast of Italy.

17. New Scotland _ _ _ _ is the central office of the London police.

18. After the dinner party, Edgar wrote a short thank-you _ _ _ _ to his hostess.

19. Professor Gordon's students complained that she assigned them too much _ _ _ _.

21. Mary's favorite _ _ _ is a doll, but her brother likes to play with his yo-yo.

22. Harold has three children, one _ _ _ and two daughers.

SOLO, DUO, TRIO: Puzzles and Games. Reproduced with permission. Copyright © 1997 by Richard Yorkey
Published by PRO LINGUA ASSOCIATES, 15 Elm Street, Brattleboro, Vermont 05301 USA 800 366 4775

Instructions

The words that fit into this kind of puzzle have been left out of the sentences given below and replaced by broken lines. Try to guess the words from clues in the context; you are not given definitions of the words. Each small blank in the broken line represents one letter in the missing word.(or words). When you guess a word, write it into the puzzle, starting in the square with the same number as the number of the clue sentence. For example, the word missing in sentence "1 across" is written across ⇨ the puzzle starting in square 1. The word from sentence "2 down" is written from square 2 down ⇩.

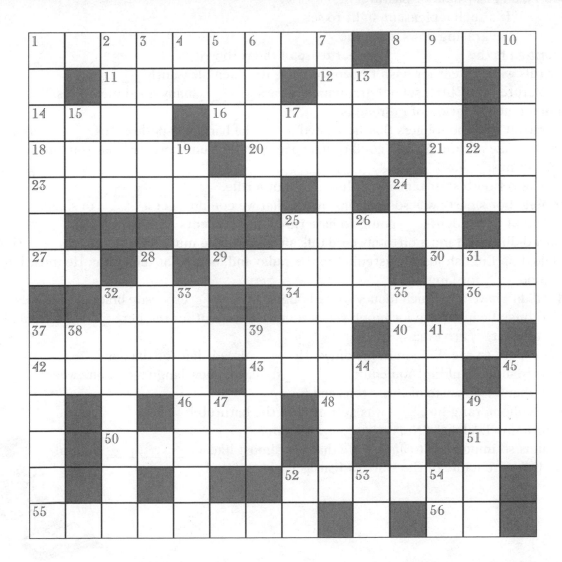

Continued on the next page.

A CLOZE WORD PUZZLE

⇨ ACROSS ⇨

1. "If I'd known you were coming, I _ _ _ _ _ _ _ _ _ _ baked a cake." [TWO WORDS]
8. "I haven't seen you for a week. Where have you _ _ _ _?"
11. "Have you ever read *Hamlet?*" "No, _ _ _ _ _ _."
12. The opposite of <u>midnight</u> is _ _ _ _.
14. "This isn't a very nice day, _ _ _ _?" [TWO WORDS]
16. "If we want to see all the sights of Washington, I think _ _ _ _ _ _ _ a car will be less expensive than taking taxis everywhere."
18. "Stop slouching in your chair! _ _ _ _ _ straight!" [TWO WORDS]
20. "Merry Christmas" in French is "Joyeux _ _ _ _."
21. In poetry, a grassy field or pasture:
    "It's such a pleasant sight to see
    The grazing cows upon the _ _ _."
23. *Has written* is the _ _ _ _ _ _ _ perfect tense of the verb <u>write</u>.
24. So far this winter weather hasn't been too cold; it's been pleasantly _ _ _ _.
25. "This picture of my high school graduation always _ _ _ _ _ many good memories."
27. A common abbreviation of <u>railroad</u> is _ _.
29. The sergeant told the soldiers that he wanted to see the barracks spotless, "as _ _ _ _ _ as a whistle"!
30. When you take advantage of a good or unexpected opportunity, we say that you "make _ _ _ while the sun shines."
32. John Wilkes Booth shot Lincoln with a _ _ _, not a rifle.
34. "Our neighbor's party was so noisy last night that we couldn't get a _ _ _ _ of sleep."
36. This class of 27 students _ _ going to have three new students tomorrow.
37. "Jessica didn't send me a birthday card this afternoon. She must have _ _ _ _ _ _ _ _ the date."
40. Ali picked up English just by listening to the radio and looking at television. He must have a very good _ _ _ for languages.
42. Shirley didn't have very much money so she bought the _ _ _ _ _ _ expensive bracelet in the jewelry store.
43. "I'm so busy I can't leave for lunch yet. You can either wait for me here _ _ _ _ _ _ me later at the restaurant." [TWO WORDS]
46. "Don't expect to see William in his office. He _ _ _ already left for the day."
48. "That is wishful thinking! You can't _ _ _ _ _ _ to learn a new language in one week!"
50. The number 34 consists of three tens and four _ _ _ _ _.
51. "The telephone rang just _ _ I was getting into the bathtub."
52. "Is your name Evelyn?" "No, _ _ _' _ _ _. It's Edna."
55. Football is so important to Jack's life that it's almost like a _ _ _ _ _ _ _ _ to him!
56. In the U.S., the name of the state of Kansas is abbreviated _ _.

SOLO, DUO, TRIO: Puzzles and Games. Reproduced with permission. Copyright © 1997 by Richard Yorkey
Published by PRO LINGUA ASSOCIATES, 15 Elm Street, Brattleboro, Vermont 05301 USA 800 366 4775

A CLOZE WORD PUZZLE #3

⇩ DOWN ⇩

1. "Don't speak too loudly. We don't want to be overheard, so we had better _ _ _ _ _ _."
2. Instead of competing, the two museums plan to _ _ _ _ _ on this project and work together.
3. While writing our compositions, we weren't allowed to ask any questions, and our teacher wouldn't even _ _ _ _ _ use a dictionary.
4. The number 505 is written _ _ in Roman numerals.
5. "Raymond, our daughter needs money for lunch at school today. Could you give _ _ _ a dollar, please?"
6. Sally said to her teacher, "I'm a good student, _ _ _ _' I?"
7. At our 25th high school reunion, we enjoyed the musical _ _ _ _ _ _ _ _ _ _ _ _ _ provided by the 1970 Student Swingtime Band.
8. One half of a French chocolate candy is a _ _ _!
9. _ _ _ _ _ _ _, the national language of countries including the United States, Canada, Great Britain, and Australia, is also used as a second language by millions of people in many other countries of the world.
10. "In the past we used to listen to the radio a lot, but _ _ _ _ _ _ _ _ we mostly watch TV."
13. Mr. Martin thinks it is important to change the _ _ _ in his car every three thousand miles.
15. When Churchill was knighted by Queen Elizabeth, he became known as _ _ _ Winston Churchill.
17. MOTHER: "Will you please mail this letter for me?" SIS: "_ _, it's too cold out."
19. "Please don't write your composition with a pencil. It's often difficult to read. Please use a _ _ _."
22. In early 20th-century New York, a train ran on tracks that were elevated above Third Avenue. New Yorkers referred to this train as the _ _.
24. Before his movie career, Arnold Schwarzenegger won the body building championship of the world. He was known as _ _. Universe.
25. In any large city, there's an underground system of _ _ _ _ _ pipes that carry away water and waste matter.
26. While we were visiting New England, we stayed overnight in a very nice old country _ _ _.
28. Just before Annie's little boy goes to bed, she throws her arms around him, _ _ _ _ him, and tells him how much she loves him.
31. "This room is too smoky. Let's go outside and get a breath of fresh _ _ _."
32. Dr. Sato's patient did not recover immediately, but day by day the doctor noticed a _ _ _ _ _ _ _ improvement.
33. A box that is empty contains _ _ _ _ _ _ _.
35. Gymnastics is a difficult sport, but Alice's coach told her not to give up. She should _ _ _ _ _ _ trying to improve her tumbling routines. [TWO WORDS]
37. Giovanni's cooking always has a strong _ _ _ _ _ _ of garlic.
38. The old English that was spoken in England from about 400 to 1100 A.D. is abbreviated _ _.
39. If you _ _ _ _ a coin in the air 100 times, it should land heads or tails about an equal number of times.
41. Johnny was so hungry that he _ _ _ three Big Macs and two large orders of French fries.
44. While dining with his present wife, George was embarrassed to meet his _ _-wife at the restaurant.
45. The new father shouted with joy, "_ _' a boy!"
47. The nearest bookstore is up the street about four blocks, _ _ the corner of M Street and 10th Avenue.
49. "I've never understood the English expression, 'It's raining _ _ _ _ and dogs'!"
52. "When you dream at night, do you dream _ _ technicolor?"
53. There is a difference between Fifth Ave. and 5th _ _. The latter is a small, unimportant street, but the former is a long, wide, well-known avenue.
54. "I've checked your work, and I think it's acceptable. I'll give it my _ _"

SOLO, DUO, TRIO: Puzzles and Games. Reproduced with permission. Copyright © 1997 by Richard Yorkey
Published by PRO LINGUA ASSOCIATES, 15 Elm Street, Brattleboro, Vermont 05301 USA 800 366 4775

Answers for the Cloze Word Puzzles

#1 Across

1. though
7. own
8. one
10. split
12. or
13. towns
15. be
16. hoe
17. used to
20. led
21. if
22. dash
23. at

Down

2. hop
3. owl
4. United
5. ho
6. herself
9. no no
10. should
11. to
14. who
15. beds
18. sea
19. to
21. it

#2 Across

1. bite
4. fast
7. anger
8. Kong
10. wise
12. elk
14. ate
15. joy
16. ivy
18. now
20. seat
22. solo
23. robot
24. eddy
25. neck

Down

1. bake
2. tank
3. Eng
4. few
5. aria
6. tree
9. olive
11. stool
13. box
16. Isle
17. Yard
18. note
19. wirk
21. toy
22. son

#3 Across

1. would have
8. been
11. never
12. noon
14. is it
16. renting
18. sit up
20. Noel
21. lea
23. present
24. mild
25. stirs
27. RR
29. clean
30. hay
32. gun
34. wink
36. is
37. forgotten
40. ear
42. least
43. or meet
46. has
48. expect
50. units
51. as
52. it's not
55. religion
56. KS

Down

1. whisper
2. unite
3. let us
4. DV
5. her
6. aren't
7. entertainment
8. bon
9. English
10. nowadays
13. oil
15. Sir
17. no
19. pen
22. El
24. Mr.
25. sewer
26. inn
28. hugs
31. air
32. gradual
33. nothing
35. keep on
37. flavor
38. OE
39. toss
41. ate
44. ex
45. it's
47. at
49. cats
52. in
53. St.
54. OK

 # Wordspell

---

Instructions

How many English words of two or more letters can you spell by using only the letters below and by following *only the connecting arrows*? For example, you can use CAP and CANE but not CANT or CANOE. After you have written as many words as you can think of, use your dictionary to be sure that each word exists in English. A total of 12 words is excellent, and 8 is good.

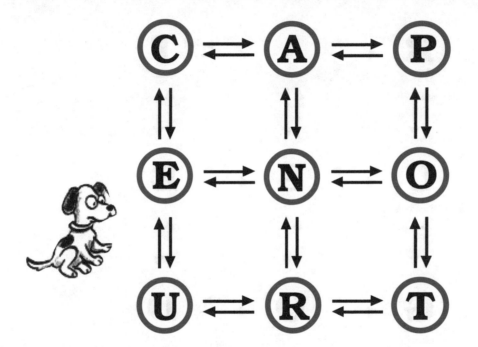

1. *cap*

2. *cane*

3. _____

4. _____

5. _____

6. _____

7. _____

8. _____

9. _____

10. _____

11. _____

12. _____

13. _____

14. _____

15. _____

16. _____

Instructions

How many English words of two or more letters can you spell by using only the letters below and by following *only the connecting arrows*? For example, you can use RAT and RATE but not RATS or EAT. After you have written as many words as you can think of, use your dictionary to be sure that each word exists in English. A total of 12 words is excellent, and 8 is good.

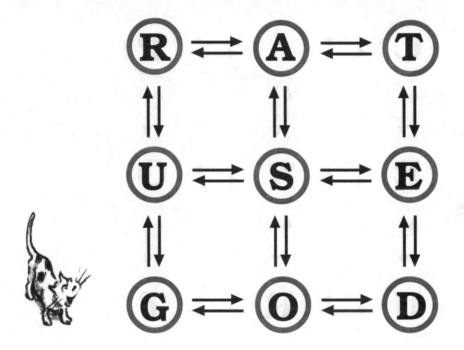

1. *rat*   5. _____   9. _____   13. _____

2. *rate*   6. _____   10. _____   14. _____

3. _____   7. _____   11. _____   15. _____

4. _____   8. _____   12. _____   16. _____

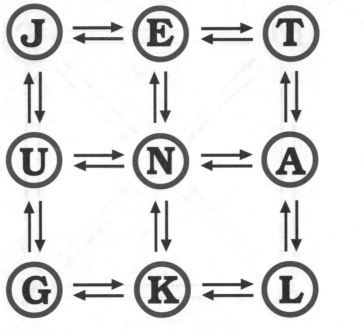

1. *ten*

2. _____

3. _____

4. _____

5. _____

6. _____

7. _____

8. _____

9. _____

10. _____

11. _____

12. _____

13. _____

14. _____

15. _____

16. _____

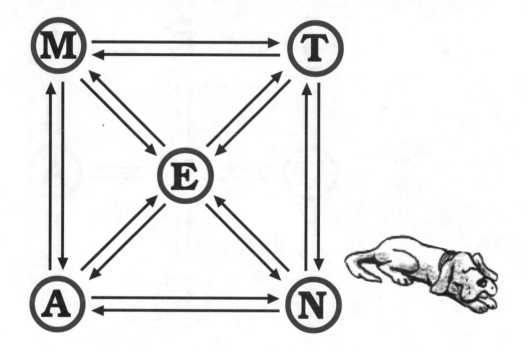

1. *an*
2.
3.
4.
5.
6.
7.
8.
9.
10.
11.
12.
13.
14.
15.
16.

At least 35 English words of two or more letters can be formed by using only the letters below and by following *only the connecting arrows*. For example, you can use TAP but not TAPE. After you have written as many words as you can think of, use your dictionary to be sure that each word exists in English. A total of 25 words is excellent, and 20 is very good.

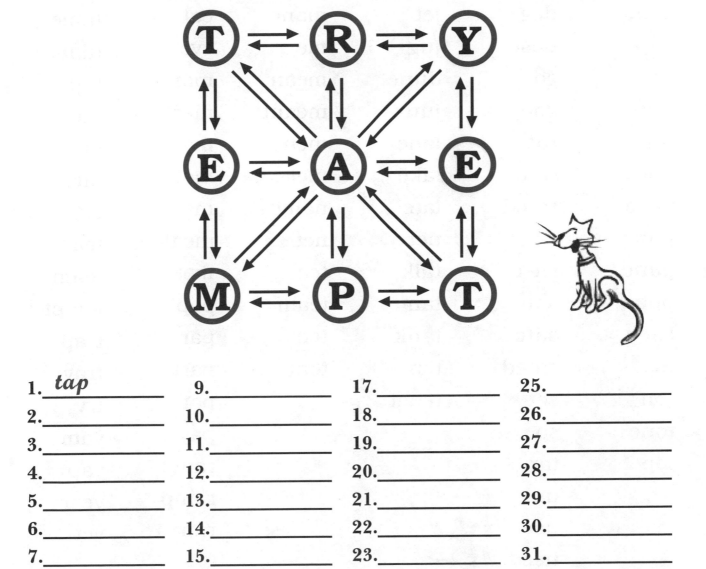

1. *tap*

2.

3.

4.

5.

6.

7.

8.

9.

10.

11.

12.

13.

14.

15.

16.

17.

18.

19.

20.

21.

22.

23.

24.

25.

26.

27.

28.

29.

30.

31.

32.

Answers for the Wordspell Puzzles

#1	#2	#3	#4	#5	
ace	as	an	am	at	rapt
an	at	at	amen	ate	rat
can	ate	gun	an	ear	rate
cane	dog	jet	mane	eat	ray
cap	dose	jug	me	eye	tame
nap	go	June	mean	mar	tamp
not	god	junk	meant	mart	tap
on	rat	lane	men	mat	tar
one	rate	lake	met	mate	tart
pace	rated	late	name	may	tartar
pan	rug	net	net	meat	tat
pane	ruse	talk	tea	met	tea
pot	sat	tan	team	pap	team
rue	sate	tank	ten	par	tempt
to	sated	ten	tent	part	trap
ton	set	tenet		pat	tray
tone	so			pay	try
top	tar			ram	yam
	us			ramp	yap
	use			rap	year
	used				yet

Break the Code

Instructions

Here are two **nursery rhymes** in English. The problem is that all the vowel letters have been replaced by numbers. Try to read the poems. Use what you know about English grammar, vocabulary, and spelling to guess what number each of the vowels is. As you work to break the code, write the vowels on the short lines next to the numbers. (For example, 1 = __) Then copy the poems on the lines at the bottom of the page.

The Secret Code

1 = ___   2 = ___   3 = ___   4 = ___   5 = ___

H2CK5RY D2CK5RY D5CK
TH4 M51S4 R3N 1P TH4 CL5CK
TH4 CL5CK STR1CK 5N4
TH4 M51S4 R3N D5WN
H2CK5RY D2CK5RY D5CK

TH4R4 W3S 3N 5LD W5M3N L2V4D 1ND4R 3 H2LL
3ND 2F SH4'S N5T G5N4, SH4'S L2V2NG TH4R4 ST2LL

_____

_____

_____

_____

_____

_____

Break the Code

> ### Instructions
>
> Here is a short joke in English. The problem is that all the vowel letters have been replaced by symbols. Try to read the joke. Use what you know about English grammar, vocabulary, and spelling to guess what each symbol stands for. As you work to break the code, write the vowels on the short lines next to the numbers. (For example, Ω = __) Then copy the joke on the lines at the bottom of the page.

The Secret Code

¶ = ___   @ = ___   Ø = ___   ◊ = ___   Ω = ___

@ B◊S¶NΩSSM@N, @N ΩCØNØM¶ST, @ND @

PØL¶N¶C¶@N WΩRΩ @SKΩD TØ @DD TWØ

@ND TWØ. "FØ◊R," S@¶D THΩ B◊S¶NΩSS-

M@N. "SØMΩWHΩRΩ BΩTWΩΩN THRΩΩ @ND

F¶VΩ," S@¶D THΩ ΩCØNØM¶ST. "WH@T

N◊MBΩR WØ◊LD YØ◊ L¶KΩ?" @SKΩD THΩ

PØL¶T¶C¶@N.

_____

_____

_____

_____

_____

_____

_____

SOLO, DUO, TRIO: Puzzles and Games. Reproduced with permission. Copyright © 1997 by Richard Yorkey
Published by PRO LINGUA ASSOCIATES, 15 Elm Street, Brattleboro, Vermont 05301 USA 800 366 4775

The Secret Code

• = ___   § = ___   Δ = ___   ≈ = ___   ◊ = ___   ∂ = ___

Δ §Δble by Δe∂•p

●nce up•n Δ t◊me, Jup◊ter, the k◊n≈ of the g•d∂, wΔlked by h◊∂ §Δv•r◊te l◊ttle lΔke. The §r•≈∂ wh• l◊ved ◊n thΔt p•nd cr◊ed •ut t• h◊m. "Jup◊ter, the §Δrmer'∂ ch◊ldren thr•w ∂t•ne∂ Δt u∂ Δnd try t• cΔtch u∂. They ∂h•w u∂ n• re∂pect. ∂end u∂ Δ k◊n≈ ∂• thΔt we w◊ll be ◊mp•rtΔnt." Jup◊ter lΔu≈hed, Δnd then w◊th h◊∂ l◊ghtn◊ng he kn•cked d•wn Δ ≈reΔt •Δk tree thΔt §ell ◊nt• the p•nd. There wΔ∂ Δ m◊≈hty ∂plΔ∂h. The §r•≈∂ were very §r◊htened by the◊r hu≈e new k◊n≈. ∂••n, h•wever, they d◊∂c•vered thΔt he ∂◊mply §l•Δted qu◊etly ◊n the ∂un∂h◊ne. Then the §r•≈∂ becΔme brΔve Δnd ∂Δt •n h◊m, unt◊l the ch◊ldren threw st•nes Δt them ΔgΔ◊n.

The next dΔy Jup◊ter cΔme bΔck, Δnd the §r•≈∂ complΔ◊ned, "Th◊∂ •ld K◊n≈ L•≈ ◊∂ ∂tup◊d. He d•e∂ n•th◊n≈ but §l•Δt peΔce§ully ◊n the ∂un∂h◊ne. Jup◊ter, ∂end u∂ Δ reΔl k◊ng!" Th◊s mΔde Jup◊ter Δn≈ry. Δ ≈reΔt ∂torm w◊nd blew d•wn §r•m the n•rth, Δnd w◊th ◊t cΔme Δ lΔr≈e, hun≈ry ∂t•rk.

"N•w, y•u §••l◊∂h §r•≈∂, y•u hΔve y•ur k◊n≈!" lΔu≈hed Jup◊ter, Δnd he ∂tΔyed t• wΔtch Δ∂ the◊r new K◊n≈ B◊rd Δte the §r•≈∂ •ne by •ne.

SOLO, DUO, TRIO: Puzzles and Games. Reproduced with permission. Copyright © 1997 by Richard Yorkey
Published by PRO LINGUA ASSOCIATES, 15 Elm Street, Brattleboro, Vermont 05301 USA 800 366 4775

Break the Code

Instructions

Here is a popular American patriotic song. The problem is that all the vowels and the consonants S, M, and B have been replaced by numbers. Try to read the song. Use what you know about English grammar, vocabulary, and spelling to guess what number each of the missing letters is. As you work to break the code, write the letter equivalents on the short lines next to the numbers. (For example, 1=__). Then copy the entire song on the lines at the bottom of the page. Can you sing it?

The Secret Code

1 = ___   2 = ___   3 = ___   4 = ___   5 = ___   6 = ___   7 = ___   8 = ___

7 1853T2F3L F7R 4P5C2734 4K284,

F7R 5618R W5V84 7F GR52N,

F7R P3RPLE 673NT52N 65J84T284

517V8 TH8 FR32T8D PL52N!

568R2C5! 568R2C5!

G7D 4H8D H24 GR5C8 7N TH88

5ND CR7WN THY G77D W2TH 1R7TH8RH77D

FR76 485 T7 4H2N2NG 485!

_____

_____

_____

_____

_____

_____

_____

SOLO, DUO, TRIO: Puzzles and Games. Reproduced with permission. Copyright © 1997 by Richard Yorkey
Published by PRO LINGUA ASSOCIATES, 15 Elm Street, Brattleboro, Vermont 05301 USA 800 366 4775

✎ Break the Code

Instructions

Oh dear! The keys on my old typewriter continually break. As I started to write this article about the alphabet in English, certain keys regularly broke and I had to use a symbol to replace the letter of each broken key. Try to reconstruct my article. In other words, use what you know about English grammar, vocabulary, and spelling and decode the English. When you decide which new symbol represents an English letter, write it in the correct box below. The first is done for you as an example.

A	B	C	D	E	F	G	H	I	J	K	L	M
						=						

N	O	P	Q	R	S	T	U	V	W	X	Y	Z

THE ENGLISH LANGUAGE IS WRITTEN WITH 26 LETTERS. ЈUT THE {ETTERS ARE &OT A{{ USED WITH THE SAME FREQUE&CY. SO#E {ETTERS ARE USED OFTE& ЈUT SO#E ARE >SED O&{Y RARE{Y. SEVERA{ {ETTERS ARE >SE? SO #A&Y TI#ES THAT IT IS ?I[[IC>{T TO WRITE A SE&TE&CE WIT+O>T T+E#. [OR EXA#P{E, T+E {ETTER E IS >SE? AЈO>T TWO

+>&?RE? TI#ES AΔ O[TE& AΔ Z, A&? AⱵO>T

O&E +>&?RE? TI#ES AΔ O[TE& AΔ J. Δ IΔ

>ΔE? T+REE TI#EΔ AΔ #>]+ AΔ G, A&? ΔI∑

TI#EΔ AΔ #>]+ AΔ]. #A&Y Δ<>?IEΔ %[

A{!+AⱵE<I] [*EQ>E&]} +AVE ⱵEE& #A?E.

ΔA#>E{ #%*ΔE #A?E Δ>]+ A& A&A{}ΔIΔ

+E& +E ?E)E{%!E? +@Δ #%*ΔE]%?E.

?%‡E&Δ %[%<+E* {E<<E* [*EΩ>E&]}

Δ<>?@EΔ A*E A{{ @&)E*}]{%ΔE

A=*EE#E&<. ◊>Δ< @&]AΔE }%> ?%&'<

¢&%, <+E #%Δ<]%##%& {E<<E* @& <+E

E&={@Δ+ {A&=>A=E @Δ E, $&? <+E {E$Δ<

]%##%& @Δ ‡. <+({@Δ< %[{(<<(*Δ @&

%*?(* %[[*(Ω>(&]} @Δ $Δ [%{{%Δ: (< $

% & * @ Δ + ? { [ ] # > = } ! Ⱶ) ¢ ∑

◊ Ω ‡.

✎ Break the Code

Instructions

This is a children's story with a moral. It was first told almost two hundred years ago to teach children in the United states to be good. To read the story, you have to break the code. Fill in the boxes with the letters that correspond to the symbols (pictures). When you have read the story, write a moral for it and compare your moral to the truism given in the answers.

Secret Picture Code

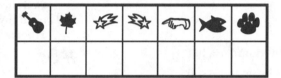

W█◆█ G♦◆◗g W█s◆█gt♦◗ w█s █ v◗◆y l█ttl◗ b◗y, ◆█s f█t◆◗ g◗v◗ ◆█m █ b◗█ut◆ful ◆█tc◆◗t █s █ p◗◗s◗◗t. W◆◗◆ ◆◆s f█t◆◗◗ w█s █w█y, G♦◆◗g l♦◗k◗d █◗◗u◗d f◗◗ s◗m◗t◆◆◗g t♦ c◆♦p d♦w◆. ◆◗ d◗c◆d◗d t♦ c◆♦p d♦w◆ ◆◗s f█t◆◗◗'s b◆g c◆◗◆◗y t◆◗◗ ◆◆ th◗ g█◗d◗◆. W◆◗◆ ◆◆s f█t◆◗ ◆◗◗ c█m◗ ◆♦m◗, ◆◗ w█s t◆◗◗ibly █◆g◆y. "W◆♦ ◆█s c◆♦pp◗d d♦w◆ my f█v♦◗◆t◗ t◗◗◆?" ◆◗ █◆◗◆◗d.

L◆ttl◗ G◗♦◆◗g◗ ◗█◆◆ to ◆◆m. "F█t◆◗◆, ◆ c█◆◆ot t◗ll █ l◆◗. ◆ c◆♦pp◗d d♦w◆ y♦u◗ tr◗◗, █◗d ◆ █m v◗◗y s♦◗◗y."

F█t◆◗◗ W█s◆◆◆gton p█ck◗d up h◆s s♦◆. "G◗♦◗◆g◗, ◆ w♦uld ◗█t◆◗ r l♦s◗ █ d♦z◗◆ c◆◗◗◗y t◗◗◗s t♦█◆ ◆█v◗ my s♦n t◗ll m◗ ◗v◗n o◆◗ l◆◗."

Answers for the Break the Code Puzzles

#1
The code: 1=U, 2=I, 3=A, 4=E, 5=O

Hickory Dickory Dock
The mouse ran up the clock
The clock struck one
The mouse ran down
Hickory Dickory Dock

There was an old woman lived under a hill
And if she's not gone, she's living there still.

#2
The code: @=A, Ω=E, ¶=I, Ø=O, ◊=U

A businessman, an economist, and a politician were asked to add two and two. "Four," said the business-man. "Somewhere between three and five," said the economist. "What number would you like?" asked the politician.

#3
The code: •=O, §=F, Δ=A, ≈=G, ◊=I, ∂=S

A Fable by Asop. Once upon a time, Jupiter, the king of the gods, walked by his favorite little lake. The frogs who lived in that pond cried out to him. "Jupiter, the farmer's children throw stones at us and try to catch us. They show us no respect. Send us a king so that we will be important." Jupiter laughed, and then with his lightning he knocked down a great oak tree that fell into the pond. There was a mighty splash. The frogs were very frightened by their huge new king. Soon, however, they discovered that he simply floated quietly in the sunshine. Then the frogs became brave and sat on him, until the children threw stones at them again.

The next day Jupiter came back, and the frogs complained, "This old King Log is stupid. He does nothing but float peacefully in the sunshine. Jupiter, send us a real king!" This made Jupiter angry. A great storm wind blew down from the north, and with it came a large, hungry stork.

"Now, you foolish frogs, you have your king!" laughed Jupiter, and he stayed to watch as their new King Bird ate the frogs one by one.

#4
The code: 1=B, 2=I, 3=U, 4=S, 5=A, 6=M, 7=O, 8=E

O Beautiful for spacious skies,
 For amber waves of grain,
For purple mountain majesties
 Above the fruited plain!
America! America!
 God shed his grace on thee
And crown thy good with brotherhood
 From sea to shining sea!

#5
The code: A=$, B=J, C=], D=?, E=(, F=], G==, H=+, I=@, J=◊, K=¢, L={, M=#, N=&, O=%, P=!, Q=Ω, R=*, S=Δ, T=<, U=>, V=), W=, X=∑, Y=}, Z=‡

64 The English language is written with 26 letters. But the letters are not all used with the same frequency. Some letters are used often but some are used only rarely. Several letters are used so many times that it is difficult to write a sentence without them. For example, the letter E is used about two hundred times as often as Z, and about one hundred times as often as the J. S is used three times as much as G, and six times as much as C. Many studies of alphabetic frequency have been made. Samuel Morse made such an analysis when he developed his Morse code. Dozens of other letter frequency studies are all in very close agreement. Just in case you don't know, the most common letter in the English language is E, and the least common is Z. The list of letters in order of frequency is as follows: E, T, A, O, N, R, I, S, H, D, L, F, C, M, U, G, Y, P, W, B, V, K, X, J, Q, Z.

#6
The code: =O, =I, =N, =H, =A, =R, =E

4 When George Washington was a very little boy, his father gave him a beautiful hatchet as a present. When his father was away, George looked around for something to chop down. He decided to chop down his father's big cherry tree in the garden. When his father came home, he was terribly angry. "Who has chopped down my favorite tree?" he roared.

Little George ran to him. "Father, I cannot tell a lie. I chopped down your tree and I am very sorry."

Father Washington picked up his son. "George, I would rather lose a dozen cherry trees than have my son tell me even one lie."

The moral: sty s th b st p l cy.

✎ Matching Like-Phrases

Like...

a million dollars (a)

a bolt out of the blue (b)   a house of cards (g)

a bull in a china shop (c)   a house on fire (h)

a bump on a log (d)   a three-ring circus (i)

a fish out of water (e)   two peas in a pod (j)

a hot potato (f)   water off a duck's back (k)

The situations:

x   Whenever I dress nicely, with a coat and necktie, my mother says that I look like __*a*__.

1. Nadim and Samir are identical twins. They look alike and, when they dress alike, they look like _____.

2. When our dog gets loose, he runs around the living room, bumping into chairs, knocking over lamps, and generally behaving like _____.

3. Henry didn't speak or ask questions in class. He only sat there silently without moving, just like _____.

4. Mary was looking for a wealthy husband, so the moment she discovered that John really had very little money, she dropped him like _____.

SOLO, DUO, TRIO: Puzzles and Games. Reproduced with permission. Copyright © 1997 by Richard Yorkey
Published by PRO LINGUA ASSOCIATES, 15 Elm Street, Brattleboro, Vermont 05301 USA 800 366 4775

Three Odd Puzzles: Matching Like-Phrases

5. When Elizabeth transferred to a new school, she was unfamiliar with the program and didn't know anyone. She felt like _____.

6. The party began to get very wild. Some people were singing around the piano, many couples were dancing to the loud music on the radio, and a noisy group was arguing about politics. The room seemed like_____.

7. After spending so much time, money, and effort building up their own business, Sally and Fred were discouraged when it collapsed like _____.

8. When Jason locked his keys inside his car, we all stood around trying to figure out what to do. Then suddenly an idea came to me like _____.

9. Pat had never met Mike before, but as soon as they met, they immediately liked each other. Now they get along like _____.

10. Molly constantly complains about her husband's foolish, expensive purchases, but her complaints have no effect. They just roll off him like _____.

✏️ A Cock and Bull Story

The Animals

bats	birds	clam	hen	ox
bear	bull	cock	horse	peacock
bee	cat	crow	horse	rat
bird	cat	dog	horses	weasel
birds	chickens	dog	mouse	wolf

The story:

Jim: Hi, Joe. I haven't seen you in a _____'s age. I'm as busy as a _____ these days. But I had some business in town and thought I'd kill two _____ with one stone and look you up. What's this I hear about your not being happy with your salesman job? Let's hear it straight from the _____'s mouth.

Joe: Hey, it's good to see you, Jim! It's been too long. Thanks for coming by. Yes, you got it right, I've quit my job. It was a real _____ race. And my boss was as mean as a _____. I don't like playing _____ and _____ with people like that, particularly when they are really as dumb as an _____! How did you hear about it?

Three Odd Puzzles: A Cock and Bull Story

Jim: Oh, a little _____ told me. But, seriously, Joe, without a job, how are you going to keep the _____ from your door? I know you're a _____ for work, but jobs are as scarce as _____'s teeth these days.

Joe: I've got a new job already! Can you believe it? I changed _____ in the middle of the stream, you might say. That's supposed to be a bad idea, but I'm happy as a _____! I had had it. That other job was for the _____. With my larger salary now, I may even be able to put on the _____ a bit. My family's happy about it too. My father's as proud as a _____, and my mother -- well, she always did think I was the _____'s pajamas!

Jim: That's great, Joe. Really great! But don't get too _____sure about your new job. You'd better not count your _____ before they hatch. If things don't go too well, you may have to eat _____.

Joe: Yes, okay. I know. I'm sure you think I have _____ in my belfry, but you'll see I'm right. I'm not going to _____ around anymore. This job will work out fine. Don't worry. Well, so long. Gotta' go now. It was nice shooting the _____ with you. See you again soon.

Jim: It was good to see you, too, old buddy. You take care, okay? Bye now.

The Beehive Puzzle

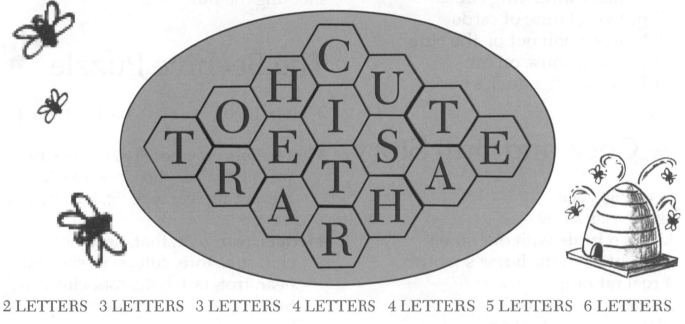

2 LETTERS   3 LETTERS   3 LETTERS   4 LETTERS   4 LETTERS   5 LETTERS   6 LETTERS

_____ _____ _____ _____ _____ _____ _____

_____ _____ _____ _____ _____ _____ _____

_____ _____ _____ _____ _____ _____ _____

_____ _____ _____ _____ _____ _____ _____

_____ _____ _____ _____ _____ _____ _____

_____ _____ _____ _____ _____ _____ _____

SOLO, DUO, TRIO: Puzzles and Games. Reproduced with permission. Copyright © 1997 by Richard Yorkey
Published by PRO LINGUA ASSOCIATES, 15 Elm Street, Brattleboro, Vermont 05301 USA 800 366 4775

Answers for
the Three Odd Puzzles

Matching Like-Phases

1-j. like two peas in a pod
2-c. like a bull in a china shop
3-d. like a bump on a log
4-f. like a hot potato
5-e. like a fish out of water
6-i. like a three-ring circus
7-g. like a house of cards
8-b. like a bolt out of the blue
9-h. like a house on fire
10-k. water off a duck's back

A Cock and Bull Story

in a **dog**'s age
as busy as a **bee**
kill two **birds** with one stone
straight from the **horse**'s mouth
a real **rat** race
as mean as a **weasel**
playing **cat** and **mouse**
as dumb as an **ox**
a little **bird** told me
keep the **wolf** from your door
a **bear** for work
as scarce as **hen**'s teeth
changed **horses** in the middle of the
      stream
happy as a **clam**
for the **birds**

put on the **dog**
proud as a **peacock**
the **cat's** pajamas
cocksure
count your **chickens** before they hatch
eat **crow**
bats in my belfry
horse around
shooting the **bull**

The Beehive Puzzle

2 letter: to, or, he, at, it, us, is, as, oh, hi

3 letters: hot, rot, her, his, hit, ate, rat, sit, cut, tea, sat, hoe, ore, toe, its, are, art, tar, ear, eat, tic, has, hat, tie

4 letters: tear, rear, that, heat, hero, chit, cuts, tore, cute, star, site, hats, hear, trot, tart, hate, rats, cite, chic, tier

5 letters: heart, treat, stare, start, cheat, chore, state, earth, heats

6 letters: hearth, cheats, hearts, treats, earths

7 letters: hearths

Note: There may be many more!